iLowerSecondary

Global Citizenship

Year 8 Workbook

Published by Pearson Education Limited, 80 Strand, London, WC2R 0RL.
www.pearson.com/international-schools

Copies of official specifications for all Pearson Edexcel qualifications may be found on the website:
https://qualifications.pearson.com

Text © Pearson Education Limited 2022
Project managed and edited by Just Content Limited
Designed and typeset by PDQ Digital Media Solutions Limited
Picture research by Straive
Original illustrations © Pearson Education Limited 2022
Cover design © Pearson Education Limited 2022

The right of Marlene Binnie and Starlene George to be identified as the authors of this work has been asserted by them in accordance with the Copyright, Designs and Patents Act 1988.

First published 2022

24
10 9 8 7 6 5 4 3

British Library Cataloguing in Publication Data
A catalogue record for this book is available from the British Library

ISBN 978 1 292 39681 1

Printed and bound in Great Britain by Bell & Bain Ltd, Glasgow

Acknowledgements

Cover acknowledgements
Shutterstock: Janna7/Shutterstock 1

Text acknowledgements
Social Change Ltd: Daisy. Equality and Equity. Social Change. 13; **United Nations Development Program:** Goal 5: Gender equality. UNDP. 27; **Problem Neighbours:** The Most Common Neighbourhood Disputes. Problem Neighbours. 59; **Tutor2u:** Conflict Geography. Tutor2u. 65, 75; **Guardian News & Media Limited:** Perfect Harmony: The Gaia Theory. The Guardian, Guardian News and Media, 27 Apr. 2008 87; **Academic Kids:** Gaia theory (science) From Academic Kids. 87; **National Geographic Partners, LLC:** Everything you wanted to know about stars. National Geographic Partners, LLC. 93; **BBC:** The life cycle of a star. BBC 93; **United Nations:** United Nations 95; **SmartCity:** Resource Repurpose: Tapping Into The Benefits Of Abandoned Places. SmartCity. 100; **University of Georgia:** Finding Reliable Sources: What is a Reliable Source? University of Georgia. 106; **Angelo State University:** How to recognize peer-reviewed (refereed) journals. Angelo State University. 106; **National Geographic Partners, LLC:** Global Warming Effects. Environment, National Geographic, 3 May 2021 109; **World Wildlife Fund:** 10 MYTHS ABOUT CLIMATE CHANGE. WWF. 110; **World Wildlife Fund:** WHY IT'S IMPORTANT THAT WE VALUE NATURE. WWF. 112; **Amnesty International:** Trafigura: A Toxic Journey. Amnesty International, 16 Aug. 2021 114; **World Wildlife Fund:** The Effects of Deforestation. WWF. 115; **United Nations Development Program:** Goal 12: Responsible consumption and production. UNDP. 116; **The Center for Biological Diversity:** 12 Ways to Live More Sustainably. The Center for Biological Diversity 118, 123; **World Health Organization:** Autism Spectrum Disorders. World Health Organization. 134; **United Nations High Commissioner for Refugees:** United Nations High Commissioner for Refugees. "Discussion Questions - Who Is a Migrant?" UNHCR 157; **Teachit Geography:** Jeans manufacture - a global case study. Teachit Geography 169; **Joseph Rowntree Foundation:** What Is Poverty? JRF, 13 Jan. 2021 175; **Houghton Mifflin Harcourt:** Eiseley, L. C. (1978). The star thrower. San Diego: Harcourt Brace Jovanovich. 179; **World Health Organization:** Access to medicines: making market forces serve the poor. Ten years in public health 2007 -2017. WHO. 194; **The Universal Declaration of Human Rights:** Resource sheet. UN 209; **Equality and Human Rights Commission:** Your Rights under the Equality Act 2010. Your Rights under the Equality Act 2010. Equality and Human Rights Commission. 214; **Equality and Human Rights Commission:** Your Rights under the Equality Act 2010. Your Rights under the Equality Act 2010. Equality and Human Rights Commission. 216; **United Nations High Commissioner for Refugees:** Who We Help. UNHCR. 229; **United Nations:** Economic and Social Council. UNDOCS. 234; **United Nations:** Economic and Social Council. UNDOCS. 234; **Anti-Slavery International:** What Is Modern Slavery? - Anti-Slavery International. Anti, 31 Aug. 2021 238; **OHCHR:** OHCHR and Good Governance. OHCHR 247; **United Nations Office on Drugs and Crime:** Katharina.kiener-Manu. Anti-Corruption Module 2 Key Issues: What Is Good Governance? 248; **A&E Television Networks, LLC:** History.com Editors. "Apartheid." History.com, A&E Television Networks, 7 Oct. 2010. 254; **Nelson Mandela Foundation:** Quoted by Nelson Mandela. Nelson Mandela Foundation. Used with permission. 257; **A&E Television Networks, LLC:** History.com Editors. "Apartheid." History.com, A&E Television Networks, 7 Oct. 2010. 258.

Photo acknowledgements
123RF: Rawpixel/123RF 19; Rafael Ben-Ari/123RF 23; Andrey_Popov/123RF 64; Audrius Merfeldas/123RF 79; Destinacigdem/123RF 92; macrovector/123RF 94; Dean Drobot/123RF 142; Dolgachov/123RF 173; **Alamy:** Brazil Photo Press/Alamy Stock Photo 38; David Jensen/Alamy Stock Photo 44; **Shutterstock:** Dotted Yeti/Shutterstock 96; 1000 Words/Shutterstock 102; Viacheslav Lopatin/Shutterstock 126; Mr. Claret Red/Shutterstock 126; Volodymyr Nikulishyn/Shutterstock 127; Alfonso de Tomas/Shutterstock 127; ChameleonsEye/Shutterstock 130; Apollofoto/Shutterstock 132; Shutterstock 142; CREATISTA/Shutterstock 144; Nanette Grebe/Shutterstock 144; Rommel Canlas/Shutterstock 146; Africa Studio/Shutterstock 147; Svetography/Shutterstock 146; Sergign/Shutterstock 153; Purino/Shutterstock 172; Kato Inowe/Shutterstock 172; altanaka/Shutterstock 172; oliveromg/Shutterstock 172; toktak_kondesign/Shutterstock 173; Eakachai Leesin/Shutterstock 173; PathDoc/Shutterstock 173; Zurijeta/Shutterstock 220; Todd Powell/Shutterstock 256.

All other images © Pearson Education

Contents

Social Justice	9
Peace and Conflict	53
Sustainable Development	83
Identity and Diversity	125
Globalisation and Interdependence	152
Human Rights	199
Power and Governance	240
Glossary	260

Welcome to Global Citizenship!

We hope you will find this book useful as you approach the exciting subject of Global Citizenship! This book will form a key part of your journey to becoming a Global Citizen. It will help you understand the wider world, your place in it, how you can engage with issues locally and globally and how you can enact positive change.

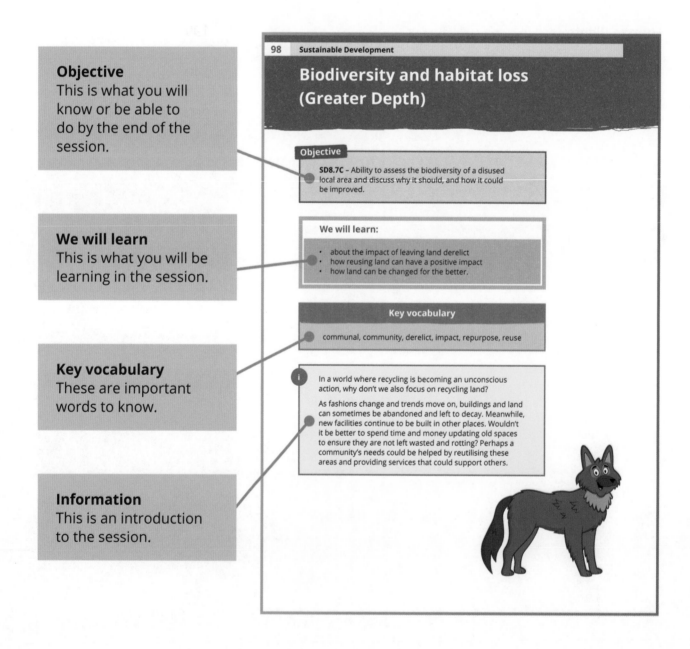

Objective
This is what you will know or be able to do by the end of the session.

We will learn
This is what you will be learning in the session.

Key vocabulary
These are important words to know.

Information
This is an introduction to the session.

98   Sustainable Development

Biodiversity and habitat loss (Greater Depth)

Objective

SD8.7C – Ability to assess the biodiversity of a disused local area and discuss why it should, and how it could be improved.

We will learn:

- about the impact of leaving land derelict
- how reusing land can have a positive impact
- how land can be changed for the better.

Key vocabulary

communal, community, derelict, impact, repurpose, reuse

i   In a world where recycling is becoming an unconscious action, why don't we also focus on recycling land?

As fashions change and trends move on, buildings and land can sometimes be abandoned and left to decay. Meanwhile, new facilities continue to be built in other places. Wouldn't it be better to spend time and money updating old spaces to ensure they are not left wasted and rotting? Perhaps a community's needs could be helped by reutilising these areas and providing services that could support others.

This book provides a clear structure to your learning. Each unit is based around a Global Citizenship strand and clearly focuses on the mastery of key objectives. These objectives are set out at the start of each unit, along with the opportunity to reflect on what you have learned at the end of each session in the unit.

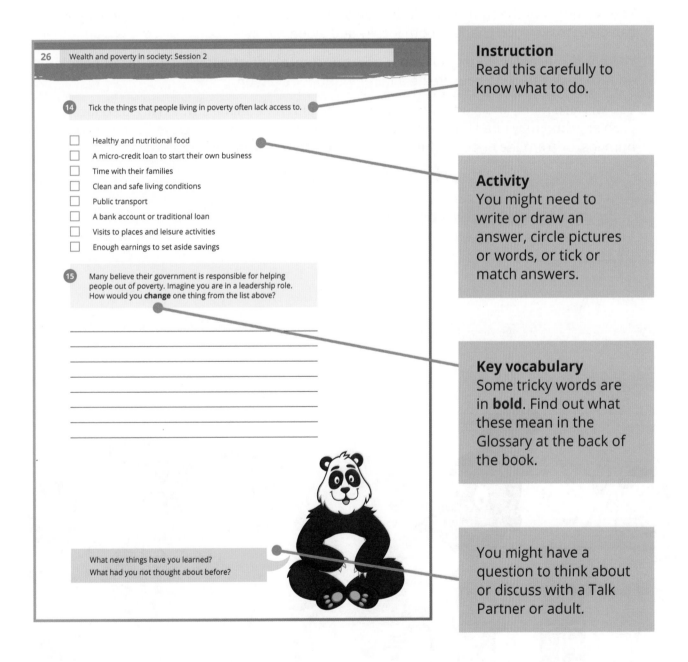

26 Wealth and poverty in society: Session 2

14 Tick the things that people living in poverty often lack access to.

- [ ] Healthy and nutritional food
- [ ] A micro-credit loan to start their own business
- [ ] Time with their families
- [ ] Clean and safe living conditions
- [ ] Public transport
- [ ] A bank account or traditional loan
- [ ] Visits to places and leisure activities
- [ ] Enough earnings to set aside savings

15 Many believe their government is responsible for helping people out of poverty. Imagine you are in a leadership role. How would you **change** one thing from the list above?

What new things have you learned?
What had you not thought about before?

Instruction
Read this carefully to know what to do.

Activity
You might need to write or draw an answer, circle pictures or words, or tick or match answers.

Key vocabulary
Some tricky words are in **bold**. Find out what these mean in the Glossary at the back of the book.

You might have a question to think about or discuss with a Talk Partner or adult.

Meet the mascots!

Global Citizens!

We are all part of a Global Community – we are Global Citizens!

In this book you will meet lots of different people. Some may seem to be like you and some may seem to be different. However, everyone you meet will have something in common with you! Some may be from a part of the world you know, or from a city, town or village just like yours. You will discover how we are all part of a Global Community and that everything we do has effects on people, animals, and the wider world.

You will find that the same issues affect all of us. This book will help you learn what you can do to make good changes both locally and globally.

You will be encouraged to think about how our choices affect different groups of people and what we can do to help create a fairer world for everyone.

You will also meet, and learn about, some of the different animals which are also facing problems and may need our help. Many of these issues come from close contact with humans, or from the effect that people can have on the environment.

The Giant Panda

Giant Pandas now only live in China and are very rare, mainly due to the destruction of the bamboo forests they live in. Protecting their habitat also helps a lot of other animals and provides them with somewhere to live. Pandas are an excellent example of the different ways people can work to help animals.

The Malayan Tapir

Malayan Tapirs are found in parts of South-East Asia. Young tapirs are dark and have stripes to help them hide when they are young. Tapirs are at risk because of hunting and damage to their habitat caused by illegal logging. Although a protected species, their numbers are still declining.

The Golden Jackal

Golden Jackals live in parts of Africa and are quite common. Because there are so many of them and they can adapt to so many different environments, they often meet people and can be found near houses and farms. We need to learn how to live safely alongside this animal to avoid future conflict.

The African Elephant

The African Elephant is the world's largest land animal and can weigh as much as three family cars! Over many years, they have often been hunted by poachers and by farmers trying to protect their land from damage. These elephants can now use only one third of the land they could use 30 years ago. Now people are learning again about how to live alongside this giant.

The Sumatran Orangutan

The Sumatran Orangutan lives in the trees of tropical rainforests. The trees they live in are being cut down for wood and the land is used to grow other things which means they are very endangered. There are not many of these animals left now but organisations are trying to protect their forests and have established sanctuaries where they can live in safety.

Justice and injustice

Objective

SJE8.1A – Know what a just society and world might look like.

We will learn:

- how to define and identify injustices
- what changes are needed in order to have a fairer society for everyone in our local **community**
- what changes are needed in order to have a fairer society for everyone **globally**
- ways in which we can help resolve social injustice.

Key vocabulary

community, equality, equity, fairness, globally, injustice, justice, opportunity, principles, privileges, society

Think of all the **privileges** and opportunities that are currently available to you. You are able to attend school. Gaining an education will allow you to develop skills you can use to get a job in the future. A job will earn you money, which you may choose to spend on a number of things you wish to own. Don't these sound like rights that everyone should have?

Now, imagine when someone does not have the same access to these privileges and opportunities due to discrimination based on their ethnicity, age, gender, or belonging to other protected groups. This is social injustice.

1   Read these statements and then complete the tasks that follow.

A Only being able to go to school with people of the same ethnicity

B Only having access to certain schools based on your parents'/guardians' income

C Being considered for a job **opportunity** based on your qualifications

D A man getting paid more than a woman for doing the same job

E All citizens being protected and supported by the authorities when they need help

F The government giving more money to schools in more affluent (well-off) areas

G Teachers grading a group of students on a different scale than the rest of the class

H Being taught and encouraged to learn at school about other people's cultures

1 Write the letter of each of the statements into these two columns.

Social justice	Social injustice

2 How does knowing these injustices exist make you feel?

_____

_____

_____

_____

_____

_____

3   Choose **two** statements from each side of the table in Question 1
    and explain why you believe they are examples of social justice and
    social injustice.

Social justice	Social injustice
Statement _____ :	Statement _____ :
Statement _____ :	Statement _____ :

In a world where there are social injustices, there can be no harmony among all of the different groups. Harmonious societies are founded and maintained on a number of **principles**.

2   Read the statement above. Think of some principles that would be necessary for maintaining a harmonious society. Add them to the spider diagram.

How to maintain harmony

3   Choose one of the principles you named in your spider diagram and answer these questions.

1   What are some barriers to this principle in society?

_____

_____

_____

2   How could these barriers be removed?

_____

_____

_____

Our **society** is continually making steps towards **equality** for all. However, being equal and fair is not always as straightforward as once thought. The notion of equality does not take into consideration that people may need different treatment to give them the same chances as others. This is called '**equity**'.

4   The image above depicts what equality looks like. Use the empty box and the definition to draw what you think equity would look like.

5   Write a speech bubble for your equity version of the drawing.

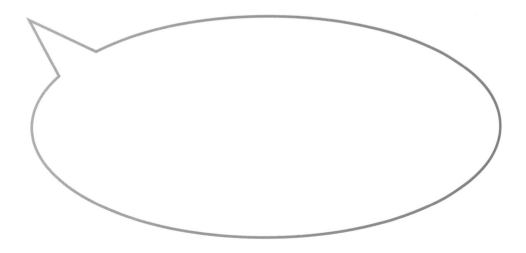

6   Fill the gaps in the text with the correct words to complete the definition of social justice. You can use words more than once.

opportunity	equity	injustice	equality

_____ means giving everybody the same thing (sameness), whereas

_____ means giving everybody access to the same opportunities (**fairness**).

In society, we cannot have _____

until there is _____ .

Focusing on _____ means recognising that the system currently in place is leaving groups of people behind and, in order to address this, resources need to be appropriately distributed to ensure everyone is able to access the same _____ and succeed at the same level without barriers.

While _____ strives to treat everyone the same regardless of need, _____ achieves fairness through providing support for people dependent on need.

When this is not happening, it is called social _____ .

7   Tick all the examples of equity in the list.

☐   Opening a scholarship application to all who wish to apply

☐   Donating a pair of shoes to everyone on the football team with the same size feet

☐   Providing ramp access to museums for wheelchair users

☐   Giving food donations to two-parent/guardian employed households and unemployed single-parent/guardian households

8   Look at the statements above that you have **not** ticked.
Explain why they are not examples of equity and suggest ways in which they may become equitable.

_____

_____

_____

_____

_____

_____

_____

_____

_____

_____

What new things have you learned?

What had you not thought about before?

Wealth and poverty in society

Objective

SJE8.1B – Understand that the nature of poverty can be complex and ways it can be overcome.

We will learn:

- to understand the complex nature of poverty
- how to consider different ways of breaking the cycle of poverty
- how to explore ways it can be overcome.

Key vocabulary

change, poverty, wealthy

i At some point, everyone needs help in one way or another. However, sometimes whether or not they are able to receive the help relies greatly on how much money they have. In today's society, money is the answer to a lot of people's problems. But what about those who have problems but not enough money to solve them?

If someone I didn't know very well asked to borrow something valuable of mine because they desperately needed it, I would first make sure they were trustworthy by...

1 Finish this person's statement by adding what you would do to check how trustworthy someone is.

_____

_____

_____

_____

_____

2 What qualities about someone would make you **not** want to lend that person your valuable belongings? Explain why.

_____

_____

_____

_____

_____

_____

3 Listed below are some qualities that define a potential lender. Which do you think is needed the most? Put the qualities into the pyramid in reducing order of importance, with the most important at the top and the least important at the bottom.

| creativity | organisation | responsibility | trustworthiness |

| collateral | accountability | imagination | mutual respect |

| honesty | loyalty |

4 Look back at your completed pyramid. Choose one quality that you placed on the bottom line. Explain why you thought this was one of the **least** important.

The quality I have chosen is _____ .

I think this is one of the least important because _____

_____

_____

_____ .

5 Now consider the quality you put at the top of your pyramid. Explain why you chose it as the **most** important.

The top quality I chose is _____ .

I think this is the most important because _____

_____

_____

_____ .

Micro-credit lenders are usually community-based organisations that provide businesses with support services and advice, in addition to financial loans.

Traditional banks provide borrowers with a loan if they have collateral. This means a bank agrees to lend a person the money they've requested in exchange for something pledged (promised) as security for repayment. In the event the person is unable to make a repayment (default), the collateral will need to be handed over.

6   Write these statements into the table according to which loan the person should apply for.

- To buy an appliance to make and sell baked goods from their home

- To buy a second house, in addition to their first house

- To refurbish their kitchen

- To buy hens to start an egg farm

- To open a convenience store for their community in a rural area

- To hire staff to recruit volunteers for a recycling initiative

Micro-credit loan	Traditional loan

7   Read Jay's story. You may want to refer back to this case study to inform your responses to the questions that follow.

Jay is 12 years old. She lives in a house on an ordinary street with her parents, older brother and younger sister. When Jay was a baby, her dad had a serious accident that left him unable to work. Although she was not injured in the accident, Jay's mum also had to give up her job to look after Jay's dad. However, Jay has noticed that their house is gradually falling into disrepair because her parents cannot afford the costs of maintaining it.

Jay's bedroom has mould on the walls, caused by damp, which has spread to the carpet and some of the furniture. As a result of this, Jay's health has suffered severely. She has developed asthma and suffers constantly from colds and coughs, which often lead to her missing school. Missing school means that Jay's education is persistently disrupted, which is having a negative effect on her attainment. She has a lower reading age than other students in her class and her overall literacy is very poor.

Even though her mum would love to help Jay with her reading and writing, caring for Jay's disabled dad has become a full-time job. In addition, the family's general health is also quite poor. Jay's mum knows that healthy food could help improve this. However, she doesn't have much time to cook nutritious meals. In addition, their food budget is very low, so they often have to rely on cheap, frozen, processed food that can be heated in a microwave.

Jay feels safest when she is at school. There, she feels relieved to be in a warm building. However, she is not totally free from worry. She has to endure being teased and picked on about the condition of her clothes and shoes. The family also began receiving state benefits, but sadly little or none of this goes towards her uniforms or school supplies. Due to her frequent absences, Jay finds it hard to make friends. Being teased often leads to her getting into arguments and fights with other children. She is too embarrassed to tell her teacher why she gets into fights. She also fears what might happen to her and her siblings if she did explain her situation. Every day is a struggle for Jay.

8   Read Jay's story and list all the indicators that show she is living in **poverty**. Briefly explain why you've chosen each indicator.

_____

_____

_____

_____

_____

_____

_____

_____

_____

9   How might Jay's school be able to help her family if she was open with them about her situation?

_____

_____

_____

_____

_____

10 Look at the people in these two images. Consider their quality of life and level of wealth. Then use the boxes to write words and phrases you think apply to each image.

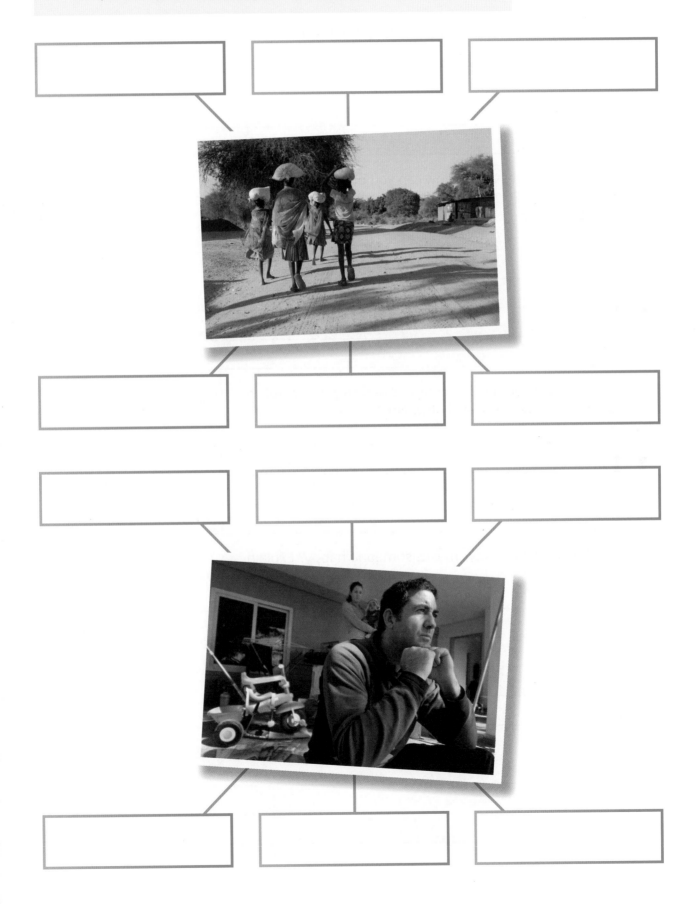

11   Look again at the words you wrote around the images in Activity 10. Then answer the questions.

1   Why did you choose these words to describe these images?

_____

_____

_____

_____

2   Based on the images alone, how can you be certain of how these people are living? For example, how can you tell whether they are poor or **wealthy**?

_____

_____

_____

_____

_____

3   What else might you need to consider before you are able to comment on someone's level of wealth?

_____

_____

_____

_____

4   Do you think wealth always makes someone happy? Explain your answer.

_____

_____

_____

_____

_____

_____

_____

12   Carefully read through each statement. Tick a box to show whether you think it is true or false.

Statement	True	False
Children growing up in households where no one has a full-time job will definitely be living in poverty compared with those in households where someone is in a full-time job.		
Two-parent/guardian families do not experience poverty.		
Children living in poverty are more likely to be ill.		

13   Choose **one** of the statements you responded to as false in Activity 12. Give your reason for this choice.

_____

_____

_____

_____

_____

_____

14   Tick the things that people living in poverty often lack access to.

☐   Healthy and nutritional food

☐   A micro-credit loan to start their own business

☐   Time with their families

☐   Clean and safe living conditions

☐   Public transport

☐   A bank account or traditional loan

☐   Visits to places and leisure activities

☐   Enough earnings to set aside savings

15   Many believe their government is responsible for helping people out of poverty. Imagine you are in a leadership role. How would you **change** one thing from the list above?

_____

_____

_____

_____

_____

_____

_____

_____

What new things have you learned?

What had you not thought about before?

Equality of opportunity

Objective

SJE8.1C – Know about some of the reasons for and impacts of inequality of opportunity for women across the globe.

We will learn:

- how women's opportunities are affected by the systems currently in place
- what changes are needed in order to have more equal opportunities for women globally
- the ways in which we can help resolve these inequalities for women.

Key vocabulary

equality, gender, inequality, opportunities

Gender **equality** is when men and women are treated equally. In today's world, there is no single country where gender equality exists perfectly. The United Nations (UN) states that 'Ending all discrimination against women and girls is not only a basic human right, it's crucial for a sustainable future.'

Imagine not being able to succeed in life simply because of your gender. This is known as gender inequality.

1   Has there ever been a time when you were treated unfairly based on your **gender**? Perhaps someone joked you could not do something because you were a boy or a girl? Write about your experiences below. Remember to include how this made you feel.

_____

_____

_____

_____

_____

_____

_____

_____

_____

_____

_____

2   Tick the statements that you think apply to women today.

☐   They receive unequal pay compared to their male colleagues.

☐   There is a lack of career progression within their jobs.

☐   There are equal job **opportunities**.

☐   Women are more likely to take a caring role as a job.

☐   Women work different hours to men because of their gender.

☐   Women have jobs that are only for them.

☐   Women are less likely to be managers.

3   Based on your own knowledge of gender **inequality**, do you think women are a valued part of the workforce? Explain your reasons.

_____

_____

_____

_____

_____

_____

4   Imagine you are in a leadership role. Create an action plan that would outline how you would tackle gender inequality in your workplace. You can use the following words and phrases to help structure your answer.

First...   Then...   After...   Lastly, continue to...

_____

_____

_____

_____

_____

_____

_____

_____

5   Read the text, look at the images and think about the speech bubbles. Then answer the questions that follow.

In a world where most women can do the same jobs as men, they currently make up less than 20 per cent of all science, technology, engineering and mathematics (STEM) careers. This concerning statistic has increased alarmingly in recent years. There are many theories as to why this is the case. Disappointingly, though, there are not many solutions.

1   Do you agree with Girl 1 or Girl 2? Give the reasons for your choice.

_____

_____

_____

_____

_____

_____

_____

2   Where might the girl you disagree with have got her ideas?

_____

_____

_____

3   If you were speaking to Girl 1, what would your response be? Write it
    in the speech bubble below.

4   Thinking of your response above, do you think Girl 1 would feel
    differently if a boy said this to her, rather than a girl? Why?

_____

_____

_____

_____

_____

As well as struggling to find acceptance and belonging in STEM careers, women also have greater difficultly earning promotion and progressing to leadership roles once in the workforce.

6   'Men make better leaders.' Do you agree with this statement? Carefully explain the reasons for your answer. You may wish to consider any countries and/or companies that have female leaders and how effective they are. (You can use the planning box to help you with your answer.)

7   Add adjectives to the diagram that describe a woman who is a leader and/or role model. Then answer the questions below.

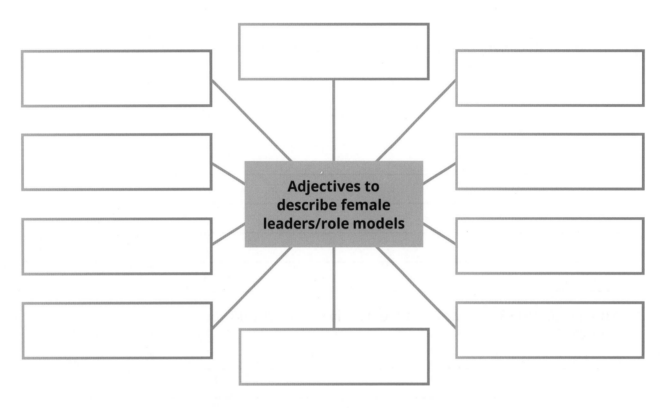

1   Which adjectives do you think are positive? Try to explain why.

_____

_____

_____

_____

_____

_____

2   Which adjectives do you think are negative? Try to explain why.

_____

_____

_____

_____

_____

_____

Some people believe that women must juggle their responsibilities in order to succeed in life. The same is not asked of men.

8   Read the statement above and then answer the questions.

1   What is your opinion on the statement? Give reasons for your view.

_____

_____

_____

_____

_____

_____

2   Who do you think might write a statement like this? Why do you think this?

_____

_____

_____

_____

_____

_____

3   What responsibilities do you think the writer suggests that women – not men – need to juggle?

_____

_____

_____

_____

_____

_____

_____

Equal rights would enable every woman to achieve her social and economic potential free from fear and discrimination.

9 Look at the potential benefits that equal rights for women could mean. Choose **four** that you feel are most beneficial and add them to the spider diagram.

Progression into leadership roles	Receiving equal pay for doing the same job as male counterparts
Progression at a steady rate in their careers	Working standard hours so they have more time to spend with family
Feeling safe and happy in their workplace	Not working three times as many hours to earn the same as male counterparts

How to maintain harmony

Read the text and then answer the question.

There was once a young girl who loved going to school. However, the leaders in the area in which she lived did not want her to go to school. They would often try to deter girls from attending.

One day, the 11-year-old girl decided enough was enough. She started to write speeches and blogs explaining that girls should be allowed to go to school, too. However, the people in power, who didn't want girls to go to school, began to notice her actions. They wanted to stop her from telling people these things.

The leaders began to worry because lots of citizens from around the world were watching and listening to what the girl was saying. So the leaders made it clear they would take action if she kept saying these things. But this did not deter her from sharing her thoughts with others.

Imagine you are the girl in this story. What would you do if someone was trying to stop you from speaking publicly about this issue?

_____

_____

_____

_____

_____

_____

_____

_____

_____

_____

_____

_____

_____

_____

_____

_____

11 Continue reading about the girl who wanted to go to school. Then answer the questions.

One day, when the girl was 14 years old, she was travelling home from school on a bus. A man armed with a gun got on the bus and shot her. The bullet missed her body but hit her head. Fortunately, she did not die.

The girl was flown to another country where she lived without fear and could access education. She continues to be a strong advocate for all girls attending school and has been awarded a Nobel Peace Prize for her efforts.

This girl was Malala Yousafzai.

Look back at your response to the previous question about this text. Now you know how the story ended for Malala, does your decision about what you would do in this situation change? What might you do differently?

_____

_____

_____

_____

_____

_____

_____

_____

_____

_____

_____

_____

_____

After the incident in Pakistan, Malala was flown to Queen Elizabeth Hospital in Birmingham in the United Kingdom (UK), which specialises in military care. After weeks of specialist treatment, Malala began her recovery and, with her family remaining with her in the UK, she continued her education. She went on to study politics, philosophy and economics at Oxford University, one of the most prestigious universities in the UK. She is now an international ambassador for girls' education.

12 How do you feel knowing that this actually happened to someone who had to fight for something many people consider to be a basic right?

_____

_____

_____

_____

_____

_____

_____

As we learned at the start of this session, the United Nations highlights the following fact: even though we are in the twenty-first century, there is still not one single country in the world where women are truly equal to men. Some of the ways to challenge gender roles are through raising awareness, educating others and changing current policies.

13   Read the text above and then answer the questions.

1   Is it important to change the fact that women are not truly equal to men? Explain your answer.

_____

_____

_____

_____

_____

_____

_____

_____

2   What do you think are some of the things we could do to change inequalities for women today?

_____

_____

_____

_____

_____

_____

_____

_____

Occurring on 8 March every year, International Women's Day is a global event celebrating the social, cultural, political and economic achievements of women from around the world.

14   Think of **three** reasons for International Women's Day to exist. List them here.

Reason 1: _____

_____

_____

Reason 2: _____

_____

_____

Reason 3: _____

_____

_____

15 Create a poster to encourage people to support and attend events for International Women's Day. Remember to include a catchy headline and some information about why it is important to raise awareness. Look back at your answers to Activity 14 to help you.

What new things have you learned?

What had you not thought about before?

Challenging injustice

Objective

SJE8.1D – Understand that there is likely to be injustice in the local area and have a desire to find out more about it and to participate in change.

We will learn:

- to define and identify what local injustices there are in our area
- to understand the potential impact we have as individuals
- about international change-makers and their impact.

Key vocabulary

Agent of Change, challenge, global, injustice, unfair

i

An injustice can occur in your life and may also be something that impacts many people around the world. Injustices continue throughout the world we live in today. Many people believe that these injustices should not exist. However, only some people are able to truly challenge them.

Some injustices can change very quickly, while others may take years to change. The trick is knowing what you can do to offer support.

1   Fill the gaps in the text to complete the definition of **injustice**.

global   injustice   undeserved

unfair   describe

_____ is the act of doing something that is deemed _____ and _____ by someone or others. The term may be used to _____ a particular event and can also be used to describe a larger _____ situation.

2   Think of a time when you saw someone being treated unfairly. Perhaps they weren't given the same opportunities as you. Explain what happened and how observing this situation made you feel.

_____

_____

_____

_____

_____

_____

_____

_____

3 Injustices occur all around us locally, nationally and globally. People who **challenge** these injustices, like Marcus Rashford, are called **Agents of Change**. Read the case study about Marcus and then answer the questions that follow. You may need to do some extra research.

Marcus Rashford is an English professional footballer born in 1997. In 2019, he set up a campaign called 'In The Box' after acknowledging the injustice of poverty and homelessness in his hometown of Manchester in the UK.

A year earlier, he and his family had started to gift boxes of essential items to those who were homeless. Then he joined forces with a business that allowed him to reach out to more people.

In 2020, the COVID-19 pandemic hit, forcing schools to close. Marcus recognised that children from low-income families who relied on hot school meals would not be able to access this necessity during school holidays. He therefore campaigned for children to continue having these free meals throughout the lockdown forced by the pandemic.

Marcus acted on these injustices by using his social media platforms and his profile as a professional football player. Although his work began in Manchester, the impact was felt across the UK as local injustices were highlighted and changes began to take place.

1   Who is Marcus Rashford?

    _____

2   What injustices did Marcus identify in Manchester in the UK?

    _____

3   How did Marcus start challenging the injustices in his local area?

    _____

    _____

    _____

    _____

    _____

4   How did he raise awareness of the injustices in Manchester?

    _____

    _____

    _____

    _____

    _____

5   Why do you think he chose to call his campaign 'In The Box'?

    _____

    _____

    _____

    _____

    _____

6   How has Marcus' campaign continued to grow?

    _____

    _____

    _____

    _____

    _____

4   Greta Thunberg is also an Agent of Change. Read this case study and then answer the questions that follow. You may need to do some extra research.

Greta Thunberg was born in Sweden on 3 January 2003. She became aware of climate change at a young age and wanted to raise awareness of the situation. Climate change is not, itself, a social injustice. However, the injustice will occur when the lives of future generations are impacted by it.

Greta first began by changing her own carbon footprint. She asked her family to change aspects of their lives that would have a positive impact on climate change. She spent a lot of time protesting against her local government. Her protest involved missing school on Fridays to sit in front of the Swedish government building with a sign that read 'Skolstrejk för klimatet' (school strike for climate). Greta actively encouraged other children to do the same every Friday. At first, she did this completely on her own. However, as this protest gained attention over social media, so the support for her campaign grew. Slowly, others began to strike all across the world, too.

In 2019, Greta left school and travelled around the world, joining people who were also striking. She made a conscious effort to travel in sustainable ways that would not impact greatly on her carbon footprint – for example, by sailing or taking the train. During this year, Greta joined many key climate conferences around the world, including the United Nations climate conference in New York, which she sailed to.

Greta has participated in many public speaking events and has challenged politicians during conferences, accusing them of failing young people. Not everyone has been supportive of Greta's ambitions. Some people have criticised her based on her age, emotion and passion. However, this has never deterred Greta and she continues to push governments to commit to cutting their carbon emissions by investing in sustainable energy.

Greta now encourages others around the world to put pressure on their governments, too.

1   Who is Greta Thunberg?

_____

_____

2   What does she campaign for?

_____

_____

3   How did Greta start her campaign?

_____

_____

_____

4   How did Greta's campaign grow?

_____

_____

_____

5   How did Greta make sure that she was heard?

_____

_____

_____

6   Are people always positive about Greta's campaign? Why or why not?

_____

_____

_____

7   Think of a name for Greta's campaign that tells people what she is aiming to achieve. Write it in the box below.

```



```

5   The texts on previous pages describe two Agents of Change: Marcus Rashford and Greta Thunberg. Look back at the texts and answer these questions.

1   What are the main similarities between their campaigns? Use examples from both case studies in your answer.

_____

_____

_____

_____

_____

_____

2   What are the differences between their campaigns? Describe some of them below, using the case studies to help.

_____

_____

_____

_____

_____

_____

3   Do you feel one campaign was more important than the other? Explain your answer.

_____

_____

_____

_____

_____

_____

6 Based on Greta Thunberg, Marcus Rashford and any other Agents of Change you may know of, list the qualities you feel an Agent of Change must have.

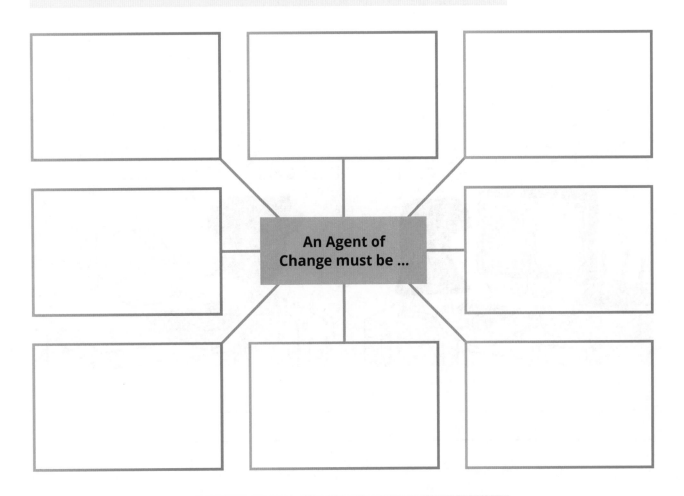

An Agent of Change must be ...

7 Look at your completed spider diagram above and then answer these questions.

1 Which quality do you feel is more important than any others you have listed to be an effective Agent of Change? Explain why.

_____

_____

_____

2 Which quality do you feel is the least important in order to be an effective Agent of Change? Explain why.

_____

_____

_____

8   In order to be an Agent of Change, you have to start somewhere. Look at the images and speech bubbles below. Which girl do you think has chosen the more proactive method to fight climate change? Explain your answer.

Girl 1: I am really upset about poverty. I know, I will post a picture of myself and say how upset I am.

Girl 2: I am really upset about poverty. I am going to research what charities and volunteering groups are doing about this issue in my local area and see if I can help.

9   To start making a change, you must first find out more. In the cases of Marcus Rashford and Greta Thunberg, these Agents of Change started by looking in their local area. Read the scenarios and match them to the possible action someone could take to help in their local community.

hunger from poverty	Donating old toys and clothing
homelessness	Raising money for charities
unemployment	Campaigning to raise awareness about food poverty in your area
mental health awareness	Volunteering at a call centre
lack of healthcare	Helping to raise money for local shelters
children in poverty	Donating suits and work clothes to suitable charities

10 Do you think every injustice will be resolved? Does that mean you shouldn't try to challenge them? Explain your answer.

_____

_____

_____

_____

_____

11 Think about your own life and experiences. Is there something _you_ could do to be an Agent of Change? Could you, perhaps, help others or change one aspect of your own life to influence change? What could this be?

_____

_____

_____

_____

_____

_____

_____

_____

What new things have you learned?
What had you not thought about before?

Conflicts in the community (Greater Depth)

Objective

PC8.4A – Know how conflict can arise within families, schools and communities; the **effects** it can have and how conflicts can be resolved.

We will learn:

- how conflict can represent itself in communities
- what can cause conflict
- possible solutions to conflicts within the community.

Key vocabulary

cause, effects, community, conflict, disputes, family, impact, solution

i

Conflict and disputes can happen at many points in your life. For example, think about when you were a child learning how to play and communicate with others. As a teenager, you may need to navigate the views and expectations of society. By adulthood, you may need to negotiate with people who have different viewpoints regarding many topics. These interactions can have great impact on both sides and others surrounding them.

Disputes and conflicts can occur among friends and in school, the workplace, communities and even globally. It is important to understand what can cause them and to know possible solutions to resolve them.

1 Think about a time when you had a disagreement with someone. Write down what happened during the disagreement and how it made you feel. Try to include what caused the disagreement.

_____

_____

_____

_____

_____

_____

_____

_____

_____

2 Match the words to their definitions.

community	To come to an agreement or decision based on a disagreement.
dispute	A clash of interests. The basis may be personal, racial, class, political or international. This can sometimes last a long time with no necessary outcome. Both sides do not compromise on their values.
conflict	A group of people who live in the same place or may have something in common with each other.
solution	An argument or disagreement between people or groups, generally regarding something that can be resolved.

Disputes tend to be disagreements that can generally be resolved. However, conflicts are rooted much deeper, with neither side wanting the other to have success.

3   Draw a line from each scenario to show whether you think it is a dispute or a **conflict**.

A friend has made a comment about you behind your back to your friends.

Your parents/ guardians have decided they want you home by 6.00 p.m. You feel this is too early. They are not willing to negotiate.

A group of older students keep gathering in the library to eat their lunch and they disturb the people studying. After involving the librarian, nothing has happened.

dispute   conflict

Your sibling has borrowed an item of clothing again, without asking.

Your partner in class keeps putting their pens and books on your side of the desk and refuses to recognise the issue.

You have a dirty or untidy bedroom space. After multiple complaints from your parents/guardians, you still think it is fine.

4   Think about whether any of the scenarios above could be both a dispute and a conflict. Explain why.

_____

_____

_____

_____

_____

Disputes and conflicts can happen among friends, **family** and in the community. Some can seem more important than others and may therefore have a greater effect.

5 Place the letters of the scenarios into the diamond based on the significance of their **impact**. Place what you think is the most significant at the top, down to the least significant at the bottom.

A Your neighbours are up all night every night playing loud music	**B** Someone has vandalised your home	**C** You disagree with your classmates about how you should deliver a group task
D Your friend thinks your favourite band is awful	**E** Your teacher gives you hard work and doesn't help you	**F** Someone is always bullying you and it makes you want to stay away from school
G Your sibling gets more attention than you and gets whatever they want	**H** Someone supports a different sports club	**I** Someone has done a favour for you; you say it is not completed properly but they say it is

6   Explain to a Talk Partner why you have placed the scenarios in this order.

7   Why do you think some people might rank the scenarios differently?

_____

_____

_____

_____

_____

There can be many causes for conflict. It is important to understand the **cause** in order to find a solution.

8   Below are just some of the causes of conflict. For each one, write a possible example of the conflict that could arise.

Poor communication	Differences of opinion
Personality clashes	Competition for resources

9   Think about the conflicts you or others may have faced. Create your own spider diagram to list the feelings (emotions) associated with these conflicts.

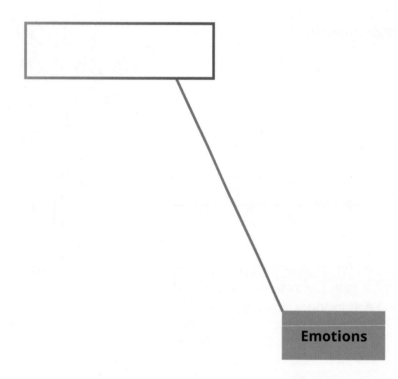

Emotions

10   Explain how you think emotions could have an impact on conflicts and disputes.

_____

_____

_____

_____

11 Read Kristofer's story and then answer the questions on the next page.

Kristofer is a young adult who lives alone in a ground floor flat. There are six other flats in the building. Kristofer's flat has everything he needs. It is close to work, the shops and other local amenities.

Life used to feel good for Kristofer. However, some months ago, new tenants moved in above him. Nothing really changed at first. Then he noticed some apple cores immediately outside of his flat. It was obvious they could only have come from the new tenants. Assuming this was a one off, he cleaned them up and thought nothing more of it. However, it wasn't long before the same thing happened again.

Over time, the issue became more serious. The new tenants began to dump their rubbish bags around the back of the building rather than correctly, using the bins. The odour from rubbish found its way into the ground floor flats and made sitting outside in the communal spaces unpleasant. As a result, other neighbours also became upset by the situation.

The tenants grouped together and contacted their local authority, which issued a fine to the new tenants. Kristofer offered to take out their rubbish for them to improve the situation for everyone. At first, this was successful. But it wasn't long before the littering issues began again.

Kristofer grew tired of constantly cleaning up and knew a permanent solution had to be reached. When he approached the tenants about the mess, they became rude and unreasonable, telling him to mind his own business. As a result, all communications between them ended – but the tenants continue to litter and the problem remains.

1   Thinking back to the story on the previous page, what type of
conflict is Kristofer experiencing?

_____

_____

_____

_____

2   Why do you think this conflict has occurred?

_____

_____

_____

_____

3   How do you think Kristofer is feeling? Why?

_____

_____

_____

_____

4   What impact would this conflict have on other people living in
the building?

_____

_____

_____

_____

5   Now think about the new tenants. What could be causing them to
act in this way?

_____

_____

_____

_____

6   In the case study, Kristofer tried to resolve the conflict. However, this did not work. What do you think Kristofer could have done differently?

_____

_____

_____

_____

7   What do you think Kristofer could do next to try to resolve the conflict between him and these neighbours? Use the case study to support your answer.

_____

_____

_____

_____

8   What do you think would have happened if Kristofer had reacted to the new tenants in the ways listed below? Add your ideas to the table.

Shouted at them	Threw the rubbish back at them	Refused to help them at all

12 Sometimes communities can offer support during conflicts. Imagine how a community (perhaps your own community) might help someone in Kristofer's situation. If there are no support plans within a community, think about what the community could do. Use the space below to write down your ideas.

What new things have you learned?

What had you not thought about before?

Resolving conflicts peacefully

Objective

PC8.4B – Ability to learn about and apply strategies for conflict resolution to their own lives.

We will learn:

- how the effects of conflict can impact resolution
- strategies which could be used to solve conflict
- how to use conflict resolution strategies effectively.

Key vocabulary

compromise, conflict, emotion, resolution

Conflict is a normal part of human life. In a world with so many inhabitants, everyone cannot be expected to agree on everything all the time. Conflict is inevitable. It is important that conflict is not something that is feared and avoided. Instead, it should be something that is resolved in a healthy way.

Resolving conflict can build a stronger, healthier relationship between people, if dealt with in the correct way.

1 Study these images for how the people are reacting to **conflict**. In the boxes beside each image, write down what emotions, thoughts and feelings you think each person would have.

2 Pick **one** image. Write what you think could happen next with this conflict.

_____

_____

_____

_____

_____

_____

Conflict **resolution** can happen when a situation of conflict reaches a peaceful resolution. It can also happen when people work to resolve an issue *before* it results in conflict.

3   Read the definition above and then answer the questions.

1   Why do you think it is important to end or prevent conflict?

_____

_____

_____

2   Do you think there would ever be a situation when it is not important to end conflict? Explain your answer.

_____

_____

_____

3   What do you think would happen if conflict was never resolved?

_____

_____

_____

_____

4   Would it be possible to live in a world where conflict doesn't exist? Why or why not?

_____

_____

_____

_____

_____

_____

4   Think about **four** conflicts you have experienced that were resolved. (You could make something up if you prefer.) Add them to the spider diagram and then explore what resolved them. Some examples have been given to help you.

Conflict with a family member	Conflict with a friend
Conflict at school	Conflict someone you know has experienced

Conflict

_____

Resolution

_____

_____

Conflict

_____

Resolution

_____

_____

Conflicts experienced

Conflict

_____

Resolution

_____

_____

Conflict

_____

Resolution

_____

_____

5   Look at the resolutions in your diagram. Which one do you think is the most effective conflict resolution strategy and why?

_____

_____

_____

_____

When conflict resolution is managed well, it helps to build stronger relationships by understanding the reasons for each other's actions. However, if it is managed badly, it can have a huge negative impact on relationships. In other words, the ways in which people react to and resolve conflict can influence how successful the outcomes will be.

6   Look at the reactions to conflict below. Write underneath each one how you would feel if someone reacted in this way to you.

Reaction to conflict: shouting back	Reaction to conflict: running away	Reaction to conflict: using physical violence
Reaction to conflict: crying	**Reaction to conflict: compromising against their will**	**Reaction to conflict: avoiding being near conflict**

There are many ways in which we can react to conflict. Some ways are healthier than others.

7 Match each unhealthy reaction to conflict with its corresponding healthy reaction.

Unhealthy reaction to conflict	**Healthy reaction to conflict**
Inability to see the person's reactions and read their body language	Calm, respectful and non-defensive reactions
Anger, rage, hurtful, resentful actions	Being able to empathise with someone else's viewpoint
Removing all **emotion**, making the other person feel abandoned, rejected and isolated	Being able to listen to, and hear, the impact this has had for the other person
Inability to see past the issue; refusal to **compromise** or see the issue from the other person's side	Being able to move forward from the conflict without holding resentment or anger
Feeling scared and actively avoiding all types of conflict	A belief that resolving conflict allows people to learn from the experience

8 What do you notice about the healthy responses to conflict?

_____

_____

_____

_____

The time you choose to resolve conflict can have a huge impact on the outcome.

9 Think about the statement above and then answer the questions.

1 Why do you think time would have an impact?

_____

_____

_____

2 What may happen if someone tried to resolve the conflict or dispute too soon?

_____

_____

_____

3 Is it possible to wait too long to resolve a conflict or dispute? Give reasons for your answer.

_____

_____

_____

_____

Conflicts can be resolved in many ways. Some people believe each side must apologise in order to resolve the conflict. However, others disagree that this is the best way forward.

Compromise allows parties to meet in the middle, with each sacrificing something in order to achieve a resolution.

10 Give your opinion about a conflict being resolved by apologising. Explain your reasons.

_____

_____

_____

11 Give your opinion about compromise as a resolution to conflict. Explain your thoughts.

_____

_____

_____

Scenario: Two people are sharing a workspace. One loves to talk non-stop about what they are doing. This really irritates the other person, who prefers to work in silence.

12 Read the scenario above. Suggest how a compromise would work as a resolution to this conflict and then outline the benefits.

How compromise would work	Benefits

13 Create a poster for others, teaching them how to resolve conflict effectively.

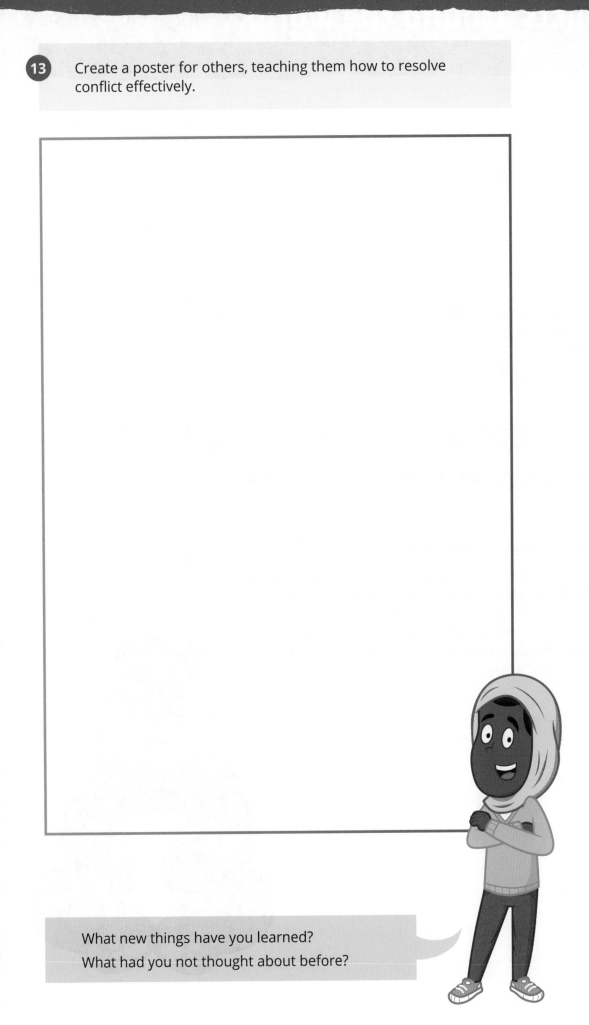

What new things have you learned?

What had you not thought about before?

Conflicts around the world

PC8.4C – Understand that conflict can lead to both positive and negative structural and political changes and innovations.

We will learn:

- about the types of global conflict
- how conflict can lead to change
- about innovations resulting from war.

Key vocabulary

change, conflict, impact, innovations, negative, political, positive, structural

i   With such a large number of people worldwide, conflict is inevitable. It would be impossible for everyone to agree about everything all of the time. Global conflict can be detrimental (harmful) both to civilians and soldiers. It can cause displacement of people, starvation and the destruction of infrastructure. These can each have a huge impact.

Conflict can lead to positive and negative political and structural changes. It can also lead to innovations that we use today.

1 Think of an argument you had with someone. Try to remember how the dispute was resolved. Use the questions below to help you with your response.

What was the outcome of your argument?

Were plans put in place to stop it from happening again?

Did other people need to get involved?

Were there agreements from both sides to stop it from happening again? If so, what were these?

Conflict can operate at a range of different levels, from a conflict with a neighbour right up to issues about climate change.

2   Place the letters of the examples below in the right boxes to show what conflict might look like at each of the levels. Add some examples of your own.

A Dispute about a major motorway expansion

B Dispute over who has authority at borders between countries

C Dispute about who should deal with a world issue

D Dispute on building a new housing development at the edge of your town

E Dispute over the quality of education in one part of the country compared with another

Local conflict	Regional conflict	National conflict

International conflict	Global conflict

3 There are many ways in which conflict can be identified in the world. Match each conflict to its corresponding example.

individual dispute	Displaying banners in public spaces to draw attention to issues
visible demonstrating of dispute	Groups rising up to overpower, disrupt and remove the government
direct action	Use of armed forces within a country to gain control or power
direct conflict	Peaceful marches and protests
mass action	Attempting to **change** the views of governments and people through extreme acts of violence
insurrection	Sitting down on the ground in front of a demolition vehicle, to stop its use
terrorism	The use of armed forces from one country against another
civil war	Writing a letter to the media expressing concern about a local issue
war	Widespread groups going on strike and protesting about policies

Conflict can lead to political and **structural** changes. These can be seen as positive or **negative**.

4   Look at these aspects of society. List the negative impacts that conflict could have on them.

Social: population, health, education, housing, crime	Economic: wealth of the country, trade, loans, agriculture and industry	Environmental: soil, vegetation, water supplies, air quality

5   List any positives arising from conflict in these areas. Explain why they arise.

_____

_____

_____

_____

_____

_____

6 Sometimes conflict can promote a **positive political** change. Read the case study about Gandhi and then answer the questions that follow.

India was under British rule from 1858 to 1947 (sometimes called the British Raj). The country was a huge asset to Britain and the British Empire. During the First World War, for example, many Indians were sent to fight for Britain. Britain believed that India could not support itself, despite its many highly educated and skilled citizens. But Indians were incredibly proud of their own culture and grew tired of British suppression. As a result, protests grew throughout the country.

Mohandas Gandhi was a key figure in resolving the conflict. Born in 1869, he grew up in India before moving to the UK to train as a barrister. Next, he travelled to South Africa to fight against the poor treatment of Indian immigrants. When he moved back to India, some years later, he began to challenge the injustices Indians faced under British rule – including repression and the effects of famine.

Gandhi, who became leader of the Indian Independence Movement, decided to use mass non-violent protests to help end Britain's rule there. He led strikes and protests, and even boycotted British goods. He was very popular with the poverty-stricken communities. He also strengthened the Indian National Congress – a political party that had been founded many years earlier.

In 1930, Gandhi sent a letter to the headquarters of the British Raj in New Delhi. In it, he outlined his plan for a campaign of civil disobedience, which would allow India to become an independent country. He made it clear that, if Britain was willing to discuss India's freedom, he would call off the campaign. The British Raj did not reply.

Over time, Gandhi's mass protests infuriated British rulers and he was imprisoned for his actions. However, prison was part of his plan. His arrest provoked more demonstrations and peaceful protests by the Indian people. Britain's rule began to deteriorate. By the end of 1930, 60,000 peaceful protestors had been convicted and imprisoned. In 1931, Gandhi was released from prison and invited to the British Raj headquarters for talks. He had served just two years of his sentence. This meeting was the turning point. From here, the British agreed how India would lead its way to independence.

1   What type of resolution did Gandhi use?

_____

_____

2   Why do you think it was effective?

_____

_____

3   Do you think this was a positive political change from conflict
    resolution? Give reasons.

_____

_____

_____

4   Who do you think might have seen this as a negative change?
    Explain why.

_____

_____

_____

5   Do you think this resolution would have been sufficient for Gandhi
    and his followers? Give reasons.

_____

_____

_____

6   Do you think people may have been against Gandhi? If so, why?

_____

_____

_____

_____

  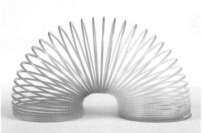

You may think that a microwave oven, superglue and slinky toys have nothing in common. However, would it surprise you to learn that these items are all **innovations** that have grown out of conflict? Innovations can be formed as a by-product of conflict because a great deal of money is often invested in new technologies during these periods.

7 All of the below inventions were created as a by-product of conflict. Rank them from 1 to 10, with 1 being the most important and 10 being the least important.

tea bags _____

blood banks _____

sanitary towels _____

zips _____

tissues _____

documentaries _____

stainless steel _____

vegetarian sausages _____

daylight-saving time _____

pilot communications _____

8 Explain to a Talk Partner why you chose this order.

9 Pick **one** invention from the last activity. Explain the impact it has had on your life.

Invention: _____

_____

_____

_____

_____

10 List some negative innovations created by conflict. You may need to research this.

- _____

- _____

- _____

- _____

11 Look at your list above. Try to rework **one** of these negative creations into a positive. Use words or an annotated diagram.

The United Nations was formed after the Second World War to ensure peace and unity among nations. It still exists today and plays a vital role worldwide. It is another example of political and structural change as a result of conflict.

12 Explain why organisations like the United Nations are often formed after conflict.

_____

_____

_____

13 Describe the benefits of organisations like this forming after conflict.

_____

_____

_____

14 Describe the negatives of organisations like this forming after conflict.

_____

_____

_____

_____

15 Do you think organisations like the United Nations would exist without conflict? Explain why.

_____

_____

_____

_____

16 Choose a conflict you know about and make notes on its **impact** - both negative and positive. (Remember that an impact can be an innovation, or something political or structural.)

What new things have you learned?

What had you not thought about before?

Planet Earth

Objective

SD8.7A – Understand the self-regulating systems of planet Earth.

We will learn:

- to understand the Gaia theory in relation to a self-regulating planet
- how the planet might self-regulate
- about the **butterfly effect** and the impact we can have on planet Earth.

Key vocabulary

anthropocentric, butterfly effect, egocentric, Gaia theory, instrumental value, intrinsic value, self-regulating, species

i Planet Earth is the only planet in the known universe able to host life. Scientists have researched and questioned this revelation over many years. Technological advancements and the ability to study other planets have resulted in many theories as to why this might be. One popular suggestion is that planet Earth is a **self-regulating** body that provides an atmosphere that allows it to sustain itself and promote life. This makes the planet seem like a living organism in itself.

A **species** is an organism that can reproduce and provide fertile offspring.

1   Write what you think about the statement below.

Human beings are more important than any other species on planet Earth. The rest of the species are there for humans to use.

_____

_____

_____

_____

_____

2   Look at this hierarchy of life. Discuss with a Talk Partner whether you agree with the order.

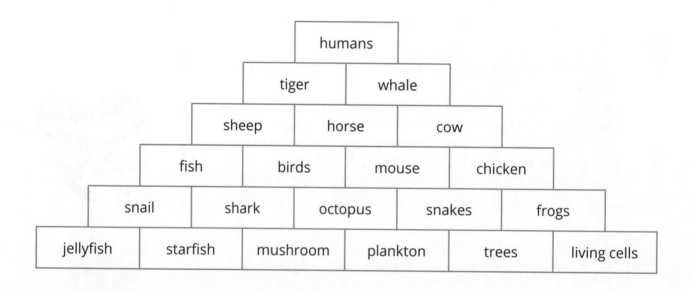

3 Look back at the hierarchy in Activity 2. Explain where you think human beings should rank themselves in relation to other species on planet Earth.

_____

_____

_____

4 Read the text below and then answer the questions.

Some people have very different views about how they see themselves and other species in the world. An **anthropocentric** view is the belief that the human race is central to the universe and everything else supports the existence of the human race. Some people believe the environment has an instrumental value to human kind – the environment is only needed for the human race to survive. However, others believe the environment has an **intrinsic value** and should be valued in its own right.

1 What could be the problem with having an anthropocentric view of the world?

_____

_____

_____

2 What is your opinion on some people's belief that the environment only has an **instrumental value**?

_____

_____

_____

3 How do you view the environment and its importance to the survival of the human race?

_____

_____

_____

_____

A theory formulated by James Lovelock in the 1980s is that planet Earth is an '**egocentric** superorganism' that is able to regulate itself. It is able to keep conditions relatively constant, enabling life to survive. The human race is not essential to planet Earth. Therefore, the belief that humankind is superior to other species and organisms is wrong. This theory is known as the **Gaia theory**.

5 Look back at the hierarchy in Activity 2. In the space below, draw what you think it would look like if it was based on the Gaia theory.

6 Lovelock suggests planet Earth is like a living organism that regulates itself. Use his theory to discuss the question: If I cut down trees or spray pesticides in the fields, would planet Earth become angry or hurt?

_____

_____

_____

_____

The Gaia theory suggests the world is able to self-regulate its temperature, atmosphere and oceans. This provides an environment that promotes survival. James Lovelock first recognised this when looking at the composition of the atmosphere.

The world's volcanoes naturally produce carbon dioxide. However, we are able to survive the natural levels in the atmosphere. The weathering of certain rocks (promoted by bacteria) break down the carbon dioxide before it travels into the sea. Algae then use the broken-down carbon dioxide. When algae break down after death, they release a gas that promotes cloud cover. This then controls the temperature of the sea, helping to cool the whole planet Earth.

7 Read the text above and then answer the questions.

1 What components do you think would contribute to the perfect environment in which organisms could survive?

_____

_____

_____

_____

_____

2 How does the world self-regulate the increase of carbon dioxide produced by humans?

_____

_____

_____

_____

_____

Planet Earth's self-regulation is a delicate natural balance that responds to the needs of the planet. Scientists have noticed that, with the increase of carbon dioxide being produced by humans, more algae is being produced in the seas around the world to help break it down.

8   Read the text above and then answer the questions.

1   Which of these impacts, caused by humans, might be stopping planet Earth's self-regulation? Tick all that apply.

☐ Deforestation   ☐ Overfarming

☐ **Recycling**   ☐ Electric cars

☐ Greenhouse gases   ☐ Overpopulation

☐ Oil spills   ☐ Chemical spillage

☐ Pollution   ☐ Planting trees

2   What other impacts can you think of?

• _____

• _____

• _____

• _____

3   Pick **one** impact from the list. How could it be affecting planet Earth's self-regulation?

Impact: _____

_____

_____

_____

4   Could any of these impacts be reduced? If so, how? Pick **one** to discuss.

_____

_____

_____

_____

_____

_____

Some people believe that events are interconnected. If something happens in one place, then a consequential action happens somewhere else in the world. This is sometimes called the 'butterfly effect' – the idea that an incident or action can have an impact elsewhere. It is thought that the small action of a butterfly's wings flapping can cause a hurricane on the other side of the world.

9 Think about all of the potential consequences of these small incidents. Add them to the table below.

Student misses the school bus	
Taxi driver gets lost on their route	
Someone incorrectly keys in their bank details when making a large money transfer	

10   While the butterfly effect may not be scientifically proven, it demonstrates that a minor action in one place can cause drastic effects elsewhere. Think about some of your own seemingly small actions and how they might have an effect in other parts of the world. What changes can you, and other people, make? Create a poster, in the box below, promoting how these small changes can help the self-regulation of planet Earth.

What new things have you learned?

What had you not thought about before?

Connecting with nature

Objective

SD8.7B – Know about the stars and planets in our solar system, including the problems associated with the space race and space junk.

We will learn:

- about planets, stars and constellations
- about the space race
- about space junk and its impact.

Key vocabulary

asteroids, comets, constellations, debris, galaxy, meteoroids, planets, space junk, space race, stars

i Since life began, humankind has observed space. Over time, and with the help of technological advancements, we have learned more and more about the universe and its expansive nature. Many space exploration milestones have occurred throughout history and are still being created today. However, our understanding of the universe is of just a fraction of the potential size of the universe itself.

Does the need to understand the universe we are in have an impact on space itself? Do we have a responsibility to tidy up after ourselves?

Our solar system is located in the Milky Way **galaxy**. There are billions of stars with planets orbiting them. That means there are potentially thousands of other solar systems in the Milky Way, too. A solar system consists of anything with a gravitational pull to the central star.

1   Tick each component you think makes up our solar system.

☐ Planets

☐ Moons

☐ **Asteroids** – small, rocky objects that orbit the sun

☐ **Meteoroids** – which range from dust grains to small asteroids

☐ Stars

☐ Dwarf planets

☐ **Comets**

☐ Central star

2   Using the information below, identify the planets in the image above.

Mars: Closest planet to planet Earth. It has volcanoes and canyons but is extremely cold.

Saturn: Known for its rings. It is a gaseous ball made up of hydrogen and helium.

Mercury: The smallest planet in our solar system and the closest to the Sun.

Neptune: Cannot be seen with the naked eye. The atmosphere is extremely cold with icy winds.

Venus: Its surface is a brownish colour due to the amount of carbon dioxide and sulphuric acid in its atmosphere.

Jupiter: The largest planet in our solar system. Contains a red spot that is a storm bigger than the size of planet Earth.

Uranus: Seventh planet furthest from the Sun. Like Neptune, Saturn and Jupiter, Uranus has rings.

Planet Earth: The only planet known to hold life.

This mnemonic gives the order of the **planets** from the Sun.

My **V**ery **E**xcited **M**onster **J**ust **S**erved **U**s **N**achos

3   Create your own mnemonic to help you remember the order of the planets from the Sun.

_____

_____

The total life cycle of a star can last billions of years. It begins as dust clouds called nebulae. Gravity forces the dust particles together, which can take thousands of years. The nebulae compact to become a protostar. Obscured by the dust around it, astronomers struggle to detect protostars.

As the protostar becomes smaller with gravity pushing the particles together, forces begin to spin it. Over a period of about a million years, this generates heat and nuclear fusion as hydrogen dust fuses together and forms helium. The helium ignites the core and a star is created. Once the balance between gravity and helium is equal, the star becomes stable. It converts its hydrogen to helium and releases a huge amount of energy. This keeps the star's temperature at 27 million degrees Fahrenheit and allows it to shine brightly. The **stars** we see today are known as main sequence stars. The Sun is an example of a main sequence star.

A star's brightness is determined by its distance from you and how much energy (or luminosity) it puts out. Colours can vary due to temperature irregularity.

4   Read the text above and then draw the life cycle of a star.

There are billions of stars in our universe. If you go out at night, you may not be able to see any. This could be due to light pollution or weather, such as cloud cover. Many ancient cultures used star patterns and configurations for all sorts of reasons. These configurations are known as **constellations**. You will see different constellations depending on what part of the world you are in and on the season.

These constellations were created by matching the stars and drawing lines between them. Many are named after mythical creatures or animals.

5   Throughout history, constellations have been used as a part of everyday life.

Tick the purposes for which you think observing these constellations have been used.

☐   To let you know the season   ☐   To give you your physical position on the world's surface

☐   To tell you the time

☐   To help you with navigation

6   Choose **one** of the purposes you ticked and explain how you think knowing the constellations helped.

_____

_____

_____

_____

7 Use the words below to complete the text about space exploration. Then use the completed definition of the **space race** to answer the questions.

rockets	warfare	moon	powerful

Soviet Union	aspirations	USA	technology

The race began after the Second World War. The

_____ and _____ were

the most _____ nations. Both nations

realised the importance of _____ as a

form of _____ and began developing

_____ which would bring about the rocket we

know today. Quickly, the nations' _____ grew

bigger and space flight to the _____ was in

their sights. The space race had begun.

1 What do you think could be some of the negative impacts of 'racing' to space?

_____

_____

_____

_____

2 Do you think either nation had the intention of exploring space further than the moon? Explain your answer.

_____

_____

_____

_____

_____

The human race has sent many objects into space, for example, satellites. However, when these objects break they are sometimes impossible to retrieve. These broken objects are often called 'space junk'. The junk can range from paint flecks to large pieces of debris.

8 List any other examples of space junk you can think of.

- _____
- _____
- _____
- _____

The United Nations states that countries have 25 years to remove old satellites from space. This does not include all other types of space junk such as **debris** and paint flecks from space junk collisions.

9 Read the text above and answer these questions.

1 If you can't see space junk and no one lives there, why is it a problem?

_____

_____

_____

2 What will be the impact on space exploration in the future if we do not clear up space junk?

_____

_____

_____

3 Who do you think should be responsible for the clean up of space junk? Why?

_____

_____

10   Use the information in this session and research your own ideas to create a poster highlighting the problems of **space junk** and the impact it will have on future space exploration.

What new things have you learned?

What had you not thought about before?

Biodiversity and habitat loss (Greater Depth)

Objective

SD8.7C – Ability to assess the biodiversity of a disused local area and discuss why it should, and how it could be improved.

We will learn:

- about the impact of leaving land derelict
- how reusing land can have a positive impact
- how land can be changed for the better.

Key vocabulary

communal, community, derelict, impact, repurpose, reuse

In a world where recycling is becoming an unconscious action, why don't we also focus on recycling land?

As fashions change and trends move on, buildings and land can sometimes be abandoned and left to decay. Meanwhile, new facilities continue to be built in other places. Wouldn't it be better to spend time and money updating old spaces to ensure they are not left wasted and rotting? Perhaps a community's needs could be helped by reutilising these areas and providing services that could support others.

1   Think about your **community** and why some of its buildings and land might be disused. Create a spider diagram for your ideas.

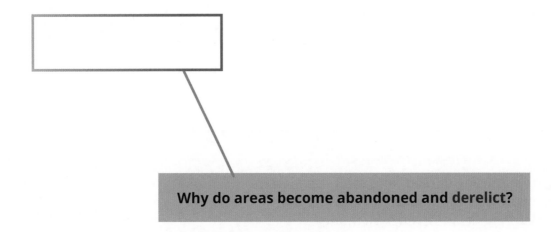

Why do areas become abandoned and derelict?

2   List the positive and negative impacts of derelict land within a community. Add **P** for positive and **N** for negative at the end of each.

Impacts on adults	Impacts on children	Impacts on nature

3 Do you think we should improve derelict areas? Give reasons for your answer.

_____

_____

_____

_____

_____

Improving and repurposing derelict land can have massive benefits. It can improve community dynamics and the surrounding environment, and even save money.

4 Read the statement above, and then draw lines to match the facts to the area that would most benefit.

| Can be 15–20 per cent cheaper than buying new land | Attracts new businesses and shops | Reduces transportation because fewer materials are used | Recycles existing structures, so saving resources |

environmental benefit   **community benefit**   **cost benefit**

| Could provide new jobs or homes, depending on the **reuse** plan | Less heavy machinery is needed, so energy consumption is lowered | Restores history that may be destroyed through neglect | Provides a safe environment for the community |

Derelict sites may have been abandoned because of a trend to move to another area. The high cost of maintaining the land or the loss of local business may also have contributed. To successfully **repurpose** a derelict site, the needs of the community will need to be met.

5   Read the text above and then answer the questions.

1   How could you find out the needs of the community that surrounds the derelict site?

_____

_____

_____

2   Whose responsibility do you think it should be to repurpose land if it has been left? Give reasons.

_____

_____

_____

_____

3   Do you think there should there be a penalty for leaving buildings empty and abandoned? What should it be and why?

_____

_____

_____

_____

4   Research any derelict sites in your local community that have been successfully repurposed. Write down your example and how it was achieved.

_____

_____

_____

_____

_____

_____

_____

6 Look carefully at the image. Then study the list of problems some communities may face. Think about what you would do with this derelict site to help improve the community's needs. Add your thoughts to the table below.

Food shortage	
Medical supplies shortage	
Homelessness	
Lack of green communal space	

7 Share your ideas with a Talk Partner. After your discussion, make any additions to your table.

8 Consider why some land repurposing could have a negative **impact** on a community. Explain why this might happen.

_____

_____

_____

_____

_____

9 Use the information in this session and research your own
ideas to design what you would build on a real or imagined
derelict space. In the top box, describe what was there initially
and how it became derelict. Then, in the bottom box, create
your new repurposed design. Add a note explaining why you
designed it in this way.

What new things have you learned?

What had you not thought about before?

Climate change

Objective

SD8.7D – Ability to critically consider information from a variety of sources and identify reliable evidence concerning climate change.

We will learn:

- how to identify reliable evidence using a range of sources
- how to use reliable **scientific data** to inform our understanding of climate change.

Key vocabulary

climate change, formats, reliable, scientific data, sources

Have you ever read, heard or seen something on the internet that seemed too good to be true? More than any other time in history, we have access to huge amounts of information literally at our fingertips. This makes research tasks easier than ever. You can find a range of sites on just about any topic you can think of. However, this also means there can be many variations of the same thing. So how do you know which information is accurate and true, and which isn't? How do you determine which sources are more reliable than others?

There is rarely just one answer to these questions. In these days, millions of people have the ability to exercise their right to freedom of expression. This means they can make their opinions public in a wide variety of ways. But how do we know which of these should be considered and which to avoid?

The question 'What is **climate change**?' was entered into a search engine. In 0.6 seconds, approximately 731,000,000 results were offered from many different **sources** in a variety of **formats**.

1 If you have access, try entering 'What is climate change?' into a search engine yourself. Look at the different types of search results. Create your own spider diagram below with different sources of information about climate change.

Sources of information about climate change

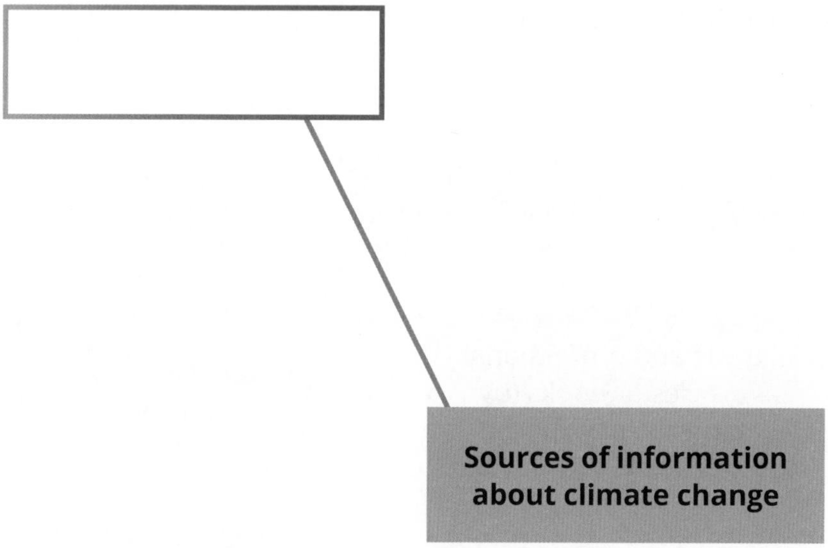

2 Look at the sources you have listed above. Explain which ones you would personally rely on for accurate information and why.

_____

_____

_____

_____

_____

A **reliable** source is one that provides a detailed, well-reasoned idea, argument or discussion based on strong evidence. Sometimes a source can be unreliable, a hoax or deliberate misinformation. Using peer-reviewed sources is one way to ensure reliability. This is because they have been written by topic experts and then reviewed by several other experts, ensuring that the work is accurate before publication.

3 Put the different types of sources into the Venn diagram on the opposite page based on whether you think they have been peer-reviewed and are therefore reliable sources of information.

textbooks

Wikipedia page

magazine articles

online blogs

health advice from doctors and other healthcare professionals

trade and professional articles or books (by experts for experts)

government laws or bills

commercial advertisements

scholarly articles and books

theses and dissertations (long essays written by university students)

social media posts

government policies

newspaper articles

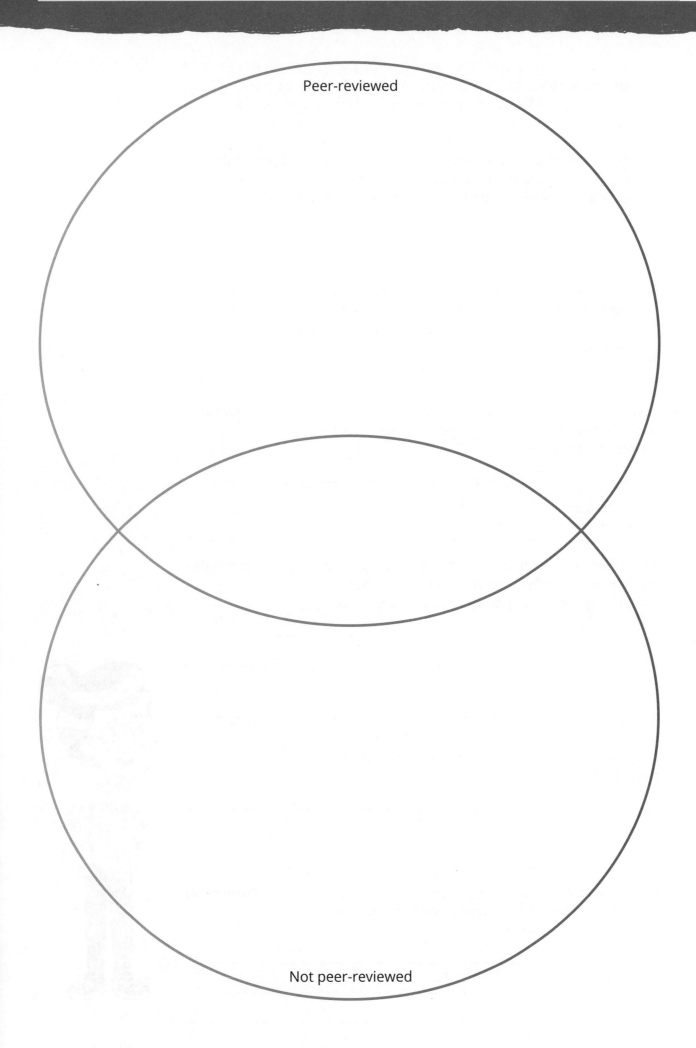

Peer-reviewed research should be clearly differentiated from reports prepared by political or commercial interest groups. In most peer-review cases, the reviewers do not know who the author is. This means the article succeeds or fails on its own merit rather than on the reputation of the author. However, if the authors are motivated by a political cause or vested (self) interest, they may select information for their report that suits their own agenda.

4   Read each statement about peer-reviewed information and reports from political/commercial interest groups on climate change. Circle whether you think it is true or false, and explain why.

Peer-reviewed publications will include all data from scientific research conducted, even if it challenges the researcher's view.

True/False

_____

_____

_____

Peer reviewers can discredit a climate change publication because it was written by an author who has a poor reputation from previous studies.

True/False

_____

_____

_____

Reports from commercial interest groups will publish information about aspects of climate change that support reasons why consumers should invest in their product.

True/False

_____

_____

_____

Reports about climate change from political interest groups always involve scientists evaluating the quality of other scientists' work.

True/False

_____

_____

_____

5 Scientists have documented the impacts of climate change on planet Earth. Match their findings with the named impact.

melting ice	Hurricanes, storms and floods are likely to become stronger and more devastating.
rising temperature	Some diseases will spread, such as mosquito-borne malaria (and the 2016 resurgence of the Zika virus); decrease in farming yield and harvest.
higher risk of drought	Global sea levels are rising 3.2 millimetres (0.13 inches) a year.
mosquitoes, ticks, jellyfish and crop pests are thriving	Increase in risk of wildfires, lost crops and drinking water shortages.
increased precipitation (rain and snowfall)	Loss of jobs, food and income for families that rely on fishing certain species for a living.
migration of species	Effect on wildlife and their habitats, with many species on the move. Some butterflies, foxes and alpine plants have migrated farther north or to higher, cooler areas.

6 Suggest some actions that can be taken to slow, or ideally stop, one or more of the impacts above.

With the climate crisis becoming an increasingly popular topic in mainstream media, there is a lot of confusion and misinformation around what climate change actually is. Therefore, it is vital – now more than ever – that you can tell fiction from fact.

7   Read the text above. Then read the statements below about climate change and tick whether you think each one is a myth or true.

	Myth	Truth
Planet Earth's climate is changing faster than ever before.		
Plants need carbon dioxide.		
Climate change isn't real, as it's still cold.		
Climate change is a future problem.		
Risk of fire in the already fragmented habitats where tigers live puts the species in more danger.		
Renewable energy is just a money-making scheme.		
Polar bear numbers are increasing.		
Renewable energy can only work when it's not cloudy or windy.		
Animals will adapt to climate change.		
Climate change disrupts the seasonal patterns of rainfall, causing droughts and/or flooding.		
Getting rid of humans will fix climate change.		
Every country is responsible for climate change.		

8   Explain why you think some of the myths in the table above became popular.

_____

_____

_____

9   Create a poster about climate change to encourage others to help save our world. Use only factual information and explain why it is reliable. Suggest some ways people can educate themselves on the issue.

What new things have you learned?

What had you not thought about before?

Energy, pollution, waste and recycling

Objective

SD8.7E – Understand how damaging many manufacturing and disposal processes are to people and environments servicing the resource-rich lifestyles of others.

We will learn:

- how damaging many manufacturing and disposal processes are to people and environments
- how these processes are servicing the resource-rich lifestyles of others
- how to explain some of the damaging personal and environmental **consequences** of these processes.

Key vocabulary

consequences, deforestation, development, disposal, energy, environmental, hazardous, manufacturing, pollution, recycling, sustainable, toxic, United Nations Development Programme (UNDP), unsanctioned, waste

i Not only is our natural world an incredible wonder, it is what makes our very existence possible. Our forests, rivers, oceans and soils provide us with the food we eat, the air we breathe, the water and earth to farm our crops – to name just a few of its resources. However, because nature is free, does that justify us taking it for granted and exploiting it? Is it right that we clear forests and overfish oceans? Does nature's unbiased accessibility give us the right to pollute rivers and build over wetlands without considering both the short-term and long term impact?

The World Wide Fund for Nature (WWF) states that, by not taking into account the benefits we get from nature, we create huge social and economic costs for ourselves. This means recognising the importance of living in harmony with nature rather than destroying it for short-term gain.

Waste is generally considered to be **toxic** or **hazardous** if it, or the material or substances it contains, cause harm. The waste may end up in the ground, streams, rivers, the oceans and even the air. It can harm humans, animals and plants. Many hazardous materials we have contact with are part of our everyday lives. Therefore, it is vital they are stored, used and disposed of responsibly.

1   Sort the materials according to whether or not they are potentially hazardous and/or toxic.

plastic bags	used nappies	thermometers	used notebook
dental fillings	car oil	batteries	wilted flowers
fridges	printer toner	solvent-based paint	mobile phones

Hazardous/Toxic	Not hazardous/Not toxic

2   Pick **one** hazardous substance/material from your table. Suggest how it should be safely disposed of. Then suggest how it should **not** be disposed of.

Should be disposed of	Hazardous substance/material	Should **not** be disposed of
_____		_____
_____	_____	_____

3   Read the case study below. Use the boxes to list how the people mentioned are affected by **unsanctioned** waste **disposal**. Add other ways you can think of in which the people and communities where this occurs could be affected.

A multinational oil trading company gathered four months' worth of toxic waste on board their cargo ship. At the end of its journey, the ship had produced a dirty petroleum product that they knew was hazardous. They tried, incorrectly, to dispose of it in five different countries: Malta, Italy, Gibraltar, Nigeria and the Netherlands. Their attempts in the Netherlands sparked an environmental incident. After some of the waste was unloaded, residents complained of the overwhelming smell and its effects, such as nausea, dizziness and headaches. One resident said, 'Why do the big industrialised countries dump in a country that has no treatment structure: it's a nastiness. We are treated like we have no value.'

It was later discovered that the oil trading company had previously rejected an offer from a disposal company to deal with the waste safely in the Netherlands. The cost would have been around US $620,000. Instead, the waste was eventually dumped illegally in Côte d'Ivoire by a local company charging just US $17,000 – a fraction of the price quoted in the Netherlands. To this day, it is still not known where all the waste was dumped.

This is the story of a company putting profit over people and a community.

Effects of unsanctioned waste disposal	

Did you know that in the time it takes to say the word **'deforestation'**, a chunk of forest the size of a football pitch will have been destroyed? That's every two seconds, every single day. With up to 15 billion trees being cut down every year across the world, this is not sustainable for people, wildlife or the climate. Deforestation affects us all, whether we know it or not.

4 Match the causes of deforestation with the demands it is carried out to meet.

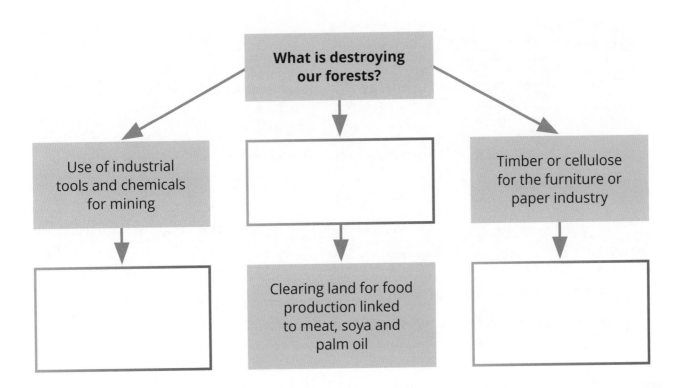

Selling gold and other precious metals for profit

Meeting global demand for cheap meat

Providing unlimited supply/choice of luxury fixtures/items

What is destroying our forests?

Use of industrial tools and chemicals for mining

Timber or cellulose for the furniture or paper industry

Clearing land for food production linked to meat, soya and palm oil

The **United Nations Development Programme (UNDP)** says that achieving economic growth and **sustainable development** requires urgent work. We need to reduce our ecological footprint, and change how we produce and consume goods and shared natural resources. The UNDP has researched some revealing statistics that support Goal 12 of its sustainable development programme: responsible consumption and production.

5   Complete the facts below by adding in the figures.

1.3 billion tonnes	22 per cent	US $120 annually

2 billion people	3 per cent

Globally, _____ are overweight or obese.

If people everywhere switched to **energy**-efficient lightbulbs, the world would save

_____ .

_____ of food is wasted every year, while almost 2 billion people go hungry or undernourished.

Only _____ of the world's water is fresh (drinkable), and humans are using it faster than nature can replenish it.

The food sector accounts for around _____ of total greenhouse gas emissions, largely from the conversion of forests into farmland.

6   In the box, write down your ideas of how you think these statistics prove that people all over the world are irresponsibly consuming goods and resources.

7 Use your ideas from Activity 6 to suggest ways in which people may be able to reduce their irresponsible consumption of goods and resources. You can write, draw or label illustrations.

8   Everything people do in their daily lives – from the food they eat to the cars they drive – has an impact on planet Earth. Match the suggested ways to live more sustainably to their positive impact on people and planet Earth.

Think twice before you buy	Fair Trade goods support companies dedicated to sustainable production and to keeping harmful pesticides out of our land and water, protecting farm workers, wildlife and families.
Go plastic-free	Reducing meat consumption can reduce the **environmental** footprint and lessen the impact of an industry that is responsible for massive amounts of water use, **pollution**, greenhouse gas emissions and habitat destruction.
Be water-wise	Using companies that generate at least half their power from wind, solar and other clean sources means that consumers are reusing natural resources instead of generating more.
Buy fair	Buying second-hand instead of new, and looking for products with minimal packaging and shipping, cuts down on waste and **manufacturing** demands.
Travel green	Walking, cycling, carpooling and using public transport whenever possible, cuts fuel emissions and can greatly reduce your carbon footprint.
Choose wild energy	Ditching bottled water and drinking from the tap (when it is safe) helps water conservation. This decreases our growing population's demand on water sources as we face unprecedented droughts.
Take extinction off your plate	Reusing bags, ditching single-use plastics and avoiding plastic packaging will help prevent birds and marine mammals dying after ingesting plastic or getting caught in it.

9 Explain which of the actions listed in Activity 8 you could start doing and the impact they would have.

_____

_____

_____

_____

_____

_____

_____

_____

_____

10 Of the things you could start doing, which do you think would be the easiest and which would be the hardest? Explain why.

Easiest: _____

_____

_____

Hardest: _____

_____

_____

What new things have you learned?

What had you not thought about before?

The future of our planet

Objective

SD8.7F – Understand and commit to living sustainably in communities and cities.

We will learn:

- how to use understanding of and **commitment** to living sustainably to benefit communities and cities
- to explain what constitutes sustainable living.

Key vocabulary

commitment, conserve, future, planet, sustainable

Although there are many ways to damage our planet, there are many more ways to protect and **conserve** it. Every individual is affected by the mistreatment of planet Earth and its resources. Therefore, every individual can also make a difference and contribute positively to a more sustainable future.

Action needs to be taken now in order to make the required changes if future generations are to benefit from the natural resources our planet has to offer before they become overwhelmed and entirely depleted.

1 Consider all the things you know about our **planet** and the state it is currently in. Then make some predictions for the **future** of planet Earth if we continue to live without making any changes. You may want to consider:

- the population
- wildlife species
- modes of travel and transport
- atmosphere and weather conditions
- technology
- peace and conflict.

Predictions for planet Earth: 2050

2 Answer these questions about your local community, or a community you know about, to the best of your knowledge.

1 On a scale of 1 to 10 (10 being 'very **sustainable**' and 1 being 'not sustainable at all'), how sustainably do you think the people in your local area live? Mark your answer with a cross on the scale below.

I   10

2 Tick the boxes in the table below to show how your community could possibly be more sustainable.

	Yes	No
Do people walk, cycle or use public transport rather than cars?		
Are there enough safe open spaces, services and cultural amenities for everyone?		
Is there enough investment in the city centres and places of leisure close to you?		
Is waste recycled?		
Are homes energy-efficient?		
Do homes use renewable energy?		

3 Based on your responses above, suggest **three** improvements that you would make to your local community. Explain the impact of these improvements.

1 _____

_____

2 _____

_____

3 _____

_____

4   Imagine you are running for a political position of power. Write
an environmentally conscious campaign explaining how you
would address the main issues concerning the future of our
planet. Use the prompts in the planning box below for support.
Then write your campaign in the box on the next page.

Suggest some stronger policies to limit greenhouse gases.
Explain how you would work with other world leaders to fight climate change.
Propose the actions you would take to protect wildlife and public lands.
Consider how you would go about providing better education on endangered species protection and the need to address human population growth and overconsumption.

5 Using your notes from the previous page, write your campaign in the box below. You could include a slogan or catchphrase to use throughout the campaign.

My environmentally conscious campaign

What new things have you learned?

What had you not thought about before?

Who am I?

Objective

ID8.2A – Understand the concept of positionality in forming our **identity** and the effect this can have on how we see the world.

We will learn:

- what positionality is and how it shapes us as individuals
- how our positionality impacts on our understanding of the world and how we view it.

Key vocabulary

identity, perspective, positionality, projection

i Think about the spaces you occupy every day and the experiences you have there. How are you treated there? How do people there interact with you? What do they expect from you? Do you think they accept you as you are?

Now imagine you are someone completely different. How do you think these changes would affect your experiences in those places?

Our personal values, views and where we live influence how we understand the world. This is called positionality.

1 Look at the two maps below and answer the questions. It might help if you imagine peeling an orange then flattening the peel by tearing, stretching and pressing it. For maps, we need to distort planet Earth's surface in the same way.

1 What might someone think of the world if they only ever saw this map **projection**?

_____

_____

2 How might their view differ if they only ever saw the world from this **perspective**?

_____

_____

_____

2 Look at the two different map projections below and then answer the questions.

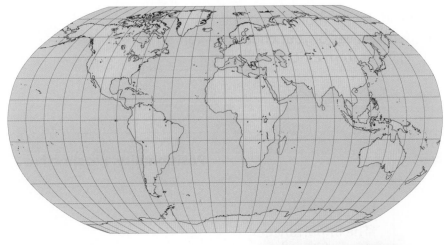

1 What do these different projections lead you to think about planet Earth? Write a comparison.

_____

_____

_____

_____

_____

_____

2 Why is it important to see things from different perspectives?

_____

_____

_____

Positionality is how we occupy or adopt a particular position in relation to others, for example, their culture, ethnicity or gender.

3 Read the statement above and then complete the table below from two different perspectives of your choosing – for example, from a boy and a girl, or from a rich family and a poor family.

Positionality: Perspective 1		Positionality: Perspective 2
	The importance of earning money	
	How you would spend your free time	
	How you would keep up with social trends	
	Your status with classmates and within groups	
	Your role within your family	
	Your future goals/dreams	

4   Look back at your completed table. Did your outlook on life change when you changed your **positionality**? How did it change?

_____

_____

_____

_____

5   Think about your future from the alternative perspective of being richer/poorer than you are now. What would such a different perspective look like? Consider the effects on your opportunities, aspirations and freedom of choice. Do you like your options?

_____

_____

_____

_____

_____

_____

_____

_____

Australia has a rich history dating back thousands of years and evolving over hundreds of generations. The peoples that have inhabited Australia for millennia are referred to as First Nations Australians. Like many others around the world, these communities maintain strong connections to their culture, language and country.

6 Use the information in the grid to complete the missing boxes in the table below.

Children are raised by their biological parents where possible; otherwise by a family member.

Punishment and peace-making processes proceed by consensus among all participants.

Generally, a person's level of contentment is measured by the quality of their relationships with others.

The land and its resources should be available for the development and benefit of humans.

First Nations Australians	Western/Non-Indigenous people
The land is thought of as being sacred and is usually given by a creator or supreme being.	
	Strangers or external parties determine the nature of a dispute or wrongdoing, and how it will be resolved or punished.
	Generally, a person's level of contentment and pride is related to how successful they feel they have been in achieving their goals.
Customary adoption occurs when childless family members are given an opportunity to raise a child.	

In Indigenous cultures, there can be many truths, depending on individual experiences.

In non-Indigenous cultures, it is widely thought there is only one truth, based on science or Western-style law.

7 Read the statements above. Which one aligns more with your perspective? Consider whether your perspective is influenced by your positionality.

_____

_____

_____

_____

_____

8 Discuss what you think you could learn from First Nations Australians.

_____

_____

_____

_____

_____

9 Think of some examples of cultural practices or traditions for your country. Explain how these examples have influenced how you view the world.

_____

_____

_____

_____

_____

In Japan, making slurping sounds when eating noodles is a way of showing you're really enjoying your food! Some scientists even say that slurping invites air into the mouth, which makes the noodles taste better. However, many societies around the world would consider it rude to eat so noisily. Positionality influences a person's understanding of what they believe is 'normal' or 'right'.

10   Read the text above and then write about what are considered 'normal' eating habits in your country.

_____

_____

_____

11   Explain how your positionality impacts how you view the world.

_____

_____

_____

_____

_____

_____

What new things have you learned?
What had you not thought about before?

Humankind: all equal; all different

Objective

ID8.2B – Wish to learn about the life experiences and choices of others in an **open-minded** and non-judgemental way.

We will learn:

- that people have different life experiences that affect their feelings, attitudes and actions
- what prejudice, discrimination and stereotyping means
- to be able to recognise our own and others' stereotypical and prejudicial views
- a willingness to listen to others, use **non-judgemental** language and respectfully consider many perspectives when discovering what makes us who we are
- to be aware of the negative consequences of prejudice and stereotypes.

Key vocabulary

autism, discrimination, judgement, non-judgemental, open-minded, prejudice, stereotype

i All around us, there are many differences, for example, in wealth, power and status. Some groups are viewed as having a lower status than others. Some have greater privilege than others. These differences lead to inequalities in our societies' systems. Where there is inequality, there is often unfair treatment directed at individuals or groups based on age, gender, weight, ethnicity, or politics. Any preconceived negative judgements or attitudes based on these groups are referred to as prejudice. Prejudice leads people to view those seen as 'other' as inferior. This often results in discrimination.

1   Fill the gaps in the text below with the correct words to complete the definition of, **Autism** Spectrum Disorder (ASD). You can use words more than once.

childhood	interests	social	repetitively

According to the World Health Organization (WHO), Autism Spectrum Disorder (ASD) refers to a range of conditions characterised by some degree of impaired _____ behaviour, communication and language, and a narrow range of _____ and activities that are both unique to the individual and carried out _____ .

An ASD begins in _____ and tends to persist into adolescence and adulthood. In most cases, the condition is apparent during the first five years of life.

2   Read the statement below. What does it suggest to you about the academic abilities of people with autism?

The WHO also states that the level of intellectual functioning in individuals with an ASD is extremely variable, extending from profound impairment to superior levels.

_____

_____

_____

_____

_____

_____

3 There are many untruths and myths about autism. Write the letter of each statement into the correct column according to whether it is true or a myth.

A All autistic children go to special educational needs (SEN) schools.

B Many people with autism feel emotions intensely and can be overwhelmed by the emotions of others.

C Stimming (repetitive behaviour like flapping or rocking) is bad and should be stopped.

D People with autism may excel in learning a lot about a topic they like, which could be anything.

E Routines can be important for people with an ASD.

F Every autistic person is good at maths, art and music.

G Most autistic children go to mainstream school, while others require support at special schools.

True	Myth

4 Repetitive behaviour like flapping or rocking can help some autistic people deal with stress and feel better. Write some things you do to cope with stressful situations.

_____

_____

_____

_____

_____

People with autism can be singers, actors, scientists, professors, video game designers and anything else!

5   Read the case study below and then answer the questions.

Satoshi Tajiri was born on 28 August 1965, in Machida, Tokyo. As a child, he was fascinated by insects and was nicknamed 'Dr Bug' by other children. Satoshi began admiring these small creatures and soon started to collect them as a hobby, which would turn out to be an inspiration for his later work. As he was growing up, the urban areas in Japan were spreading. This meant more and more land was gradually paved over, and habitats for hunting bugs were lost. Little did the children who gave him the nickname know that he would turn his fixation into a worldwide phenomenon.

As a teenager, Satoshi developed another fascination: video games. His interest led him to develop his own games. Later, he merged his two passions together and created a game that allowed children to have the same feeling of catching and collecting creatures as he had when he was a child. This game was the world-renowned Pokémon.

1   What behaviours were early indications of an ASD in Satoshi Tajiri's story?

_____

_____

_____

2   How might his ASD have contributed to his success?

_____

_____

_____

_____

6 In today's society, people can be judged for anything. Think of some characteristics for which someone might judge another or be judged themselves. Add them to the spider diagram.

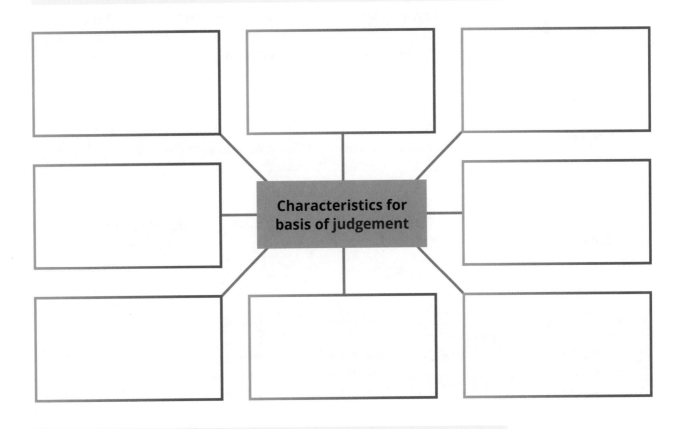

7 Describe a time when you felt as though you were unfairly judged – particularly by someone who did not know you very well or at all.

_____

_____

_____

_____

8 Think about whether you have ever judged someone else and realised later that your judgement was unfair. Describe how that might have made you feel.

_____

_____

_____

9 Match the words to their definitions.

discrimination	Comes from the words 'to judge before'. It is the formation of an unfavourable opinion or feeling about a person or a group of people without a full examination of them.
prejudice	Making oversimplified generalisations about people who belong to a certain group and labelling them based on this.
stereotype	Treatment or action against an individual based on the group, class or category they belong to, disregarding their individual merits.

The meanings of 'prejudice' and 'discrimination' are often confused. A simple distinction is that 'prejudice' is to do with attitude and 'discrimination' is to do with action.

10 Think of an example for 'prejudice' and one for 'discrimination' that would help people differentiate between the two. Add these to the table.

Prejudice	Discrimination

11 Stereotypes can be founded on a range of different characteristics. Add some stereotypes for each of the characteristics in the table below.

Age	
Ethnicity	
Gender	
Country of origin	
Family history	

12 Choose **one** of your examples from Activity 11. Write an explanation for why this generalisation may have been established. Include what type of person might have popularised it.

_____

_____

_____

_____

_____

_____

_____

_____

13 Write about yourself as a stereotypical person of your gender by completing these statements.

My favourite colour is _____ .

My favourite sport is _____ .

My favourite thing to wear is _____ .

My favourite thing to do is _____ .

When I am older I want to be _____ .

14 Explain whether the stereotypical statements you wrote match with the real you.

_____

_____

_____

15 Look at this stereotypical image of a boy. Now draw him doing something people would not expect him to do.

People think that because I'm a boy, I should only enjoy doing things like this.

What new things have you learned?

What had you not thought about before?

Challenging prejudice and discrimination

Objective

ID8.2C – Ability to empathise with people who are treated unfairly in society and seek to understand and challenge structures that cause this.

We will learn:

- to show **empathy** towards people who are treated unfairly
- to identify **structures** and **systems** that caused this unfair treatment in the past and those that cause it now.

Key vocabulary

empathy, prejudice, society, structures, systems

i Imagine waking up one day and being favoured for the colour of your hair – nothing else. People respect you and value your place in society. Your intelligence is rarely questioned. You are seldom suspected or accused of violent, anti-social behaviour. Most people are kind and friendly towards you even when they don't know you. How would that feel?

Now imagine waking up the next morning and being mistreated because of your hair colour. How would this change your experience from the day before?

Society often has a lot to say about how other people should live their lives. This is usually dependent on what group an individual belongs to, their appearance, where they live and many other things.

1. Look at the image of a doctor. What might this doctor say about the opinions of others with regards to women working in this profession? Write your answer in the speech bubble.

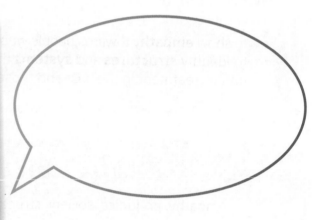

2. Now look at the image of a boxer. What might this boxer say about the opinions of others with regards to men working in this profession? Write your answer in the speech bubble.

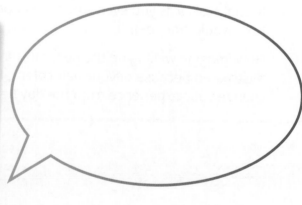

3 Read your two speech bubbles again and then answer these questions.

1 How do your speech bubbles differ?

_____

_____

_____

2 How can these differences be used as a reflection of society's ideas of gender norms?

_____

_____

_____

_____

3 What can you tell about someone based only on their hobbies and interests? If possible, give some examples.

_____

_____

_____

_____

_____

4 What can you **not** tell about someone based only on their hobbies and interests? Give examples.

_____

_____

_____

_____

_____

5 What assumptions might people might make about you because of your hobbies or the things you enjoy doing? Tick any assumptions that are true.

☐ _____

☐ _____

☐ _____

☐ _____

☐ _____

4   Look at the images of the dancers. Society is likely to be more accepting of one of these. Write which one you think it is and explain your reasons why.

_____

_____

_____

_____

_____

Some people have negative opinions about male dancers in any genre. Prejudiced comments are sometimes made about these men and their characters, ignoring the difficulty and skill that goes into what they do.

5 List the qualities that the dancers in both images need to possess in order to perform.

- _____
- _____
- _____
- _____
- _____

- _____
- _____
- _____
- _____
- _____

6 Some people think certain sports/activities are only for girls and others are for boys. List some sports and activities that people typically align with a gender.

Boys	Girls

Pretty boys, afraid to get their hands dirty with honest labour.

They're so cool, and the skills they have are so impressive.

7 Look at the images and comments. These men are using the same skill level and dedication. Yet, society may view them differently.

1 Write **one** difference that people might comment on in a prejudiced or stereotypical way.

_____

_____

_____

2 Write in the speech bubble a description of both images using non-judgemental language.

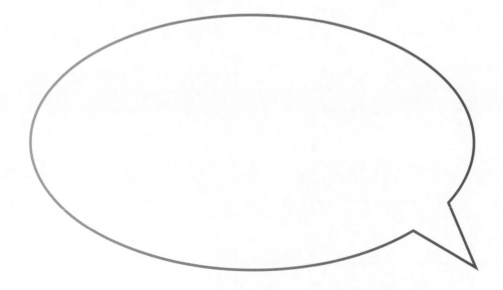

8   Read the statements in the table and then look at the questions.

Statements	Fact	Opinion
Women are legally allowed to drive in every country in the world.		
All women are bad at parking.		
Women shouldn't be taxi drivers because they always get lost.		

1   Tick to show whether you think each statement is a fact or an opinion.

2   Choose **one** statement and explain why you said it was fact or opinion.

_____

_____

_____

_____

9   Read the newspaper article and answer the questions that follow.

Two male sports presenters have been accused of sexism after commenting on a referee that was a woman. During a football match, they criticised her lack of knowledge, in their opinion, on the offside rule (an important football rule). The commentators, who believed their microphones were off, were actually recorded making remarks such as, 'Someone better get down there and explain offside to her' and 'Can you believe that? A female referee? Women don't know the offside rule.'

1   What is the prejudiced attitude?

_____

2   Who is the **prejudice** directed towards?

_____

3   How might the prejudiced attitude impact on the woman concerned and other women in similar roles?

_____

_____

_____

4   What prejudiced attitudes are these stereotypes based on?

_____

_____

_____

5   What assumptions are being made about the woman and her ability to perform her role?

_____

_____

_____

6   How would you feel if you were treated this way for doing your job in the way you'd been trained?

_____

_____

_____

_____

10   Read the text and answer the questions on this and the
following page.

> In 1962, the United States of America (USA) decided to send
> people to the Moon. However, getting there and back would be
> hard work and require many problems to be solved. In order to
> do this, the National Aeronautics and Space Administration (NASA)
> created large teams of mathematicians and scientists to work on
> this incredible project as 'human computers'.
>
> The first time Katherine Johnson, a 34-year-old African-American
> college graduate, applied for a job on this project she did not
> get it.
>
> Johnson applied again the following year and was successful. She
> studied how to use geometry for space travel and was responsible
> for calculating the paths for the spacecraft to orbit planet Earth
> and land on the Moon. NASA used Johnson's maths – and it
> worked! Thanks to her calculations, NASA sent astronauts into
> orbit around planet Earth and was later able to send astronauts to
> the Moon and back.

1   What do you think is the average person's idea of the mathematicians
and scientists that NASA was looking for? Write your thoughts in
the table.

Gender	
Ethnicity	
Nationality	

2   What prejudicial ideas that may have been prominent in the USA in the 1960s could explain why Katherine Johnson was not hired the first time?

_____

_____

_____

_____

3   How vital was Katherine Johnson's role in the monumental Moon landing? Would it have been possible if NASA hadn't put their prejudice aside?

_____

_____

_____

_____

4   Have you ever heard of Katherine Johnson? Considering the huge role she played in such a historical moment, do you think she has been given the recognition she deserves?

_____

_____

_____

_____

5   Do you think this would be different if Katherine Johnson was a different gender or ethnicity? Explain your reasons.

_____

_____

_____

6   Do you think it would be different if Katherine Johnson had made this accomplishment today? Or do you think society's views are still the same or similar to how they were in the 1960s?

_____

_____

_____

11   Read the stereotypes and choose **three**. Explain how your chosen statements make you feel. Add why you think it is untrue and unfair to label all people in a group like this.

A woman's place is at home.	All Black people are good at sports.
Boys who wear hoodies are in a gang.	Older people do not like technology.
Women are better at showing their emotions than men.	Boys who cry are weak.

Stereotype	This makes me feel...	It is untrue/unfair because...

What new things have you learned?

What had you not thought about before?

People and places around the world

Objective

GI8.3A – Know some of the reasons that people travel and why they move to different countries.

We will learn:

- the history of human migration
- the reasons why people travel
- how migration has affected us.

Key vocabulary

asylum seekers, heritage, internally displaced, migration, poverty, refugees

i

Humans have been travelling for hundreds of thousands of years. This has had an impact on the way we live, what we know and the experiences we have had as human beings. Some people travel for fun; others travel out of necessity and in search of safety. Many people seek opportunity or simply the thrill of the unknown. All these scenarios have helped form new experiences and understanding as a human race.

Travelling to new countries for work or an alternative lifestyle is called migration. If you are able to, look back through your heritage. Do you live in the country your heritage is derived from?

1   Read the text and then tick why you think humans travelled.

The earliest record of our species dates back 200,000 years ago to Africa. Since then, humans have travelled and migrated around the globe. First, they headed to Asia and Australia. Then they travelled to Russia and Europe. When the great ice came down from the North, this connected what is now Europe to the Americas, so humans then began to travel to the Americas.

☐ For work

☐ For food

☐ For water

☐ For friends and family

☐ For adventure-seeking thrills

☐ For suitable weather

☐ To be the first to circumnavigate the world

2   Pick any **two** options you ticked and explain your reasons for ticking them.

1 _____

_____

_____

2 _____

_____

_____

3 These days, many people travel to locations all around the world. Complete this spider diagram with the reasons someone might travel.

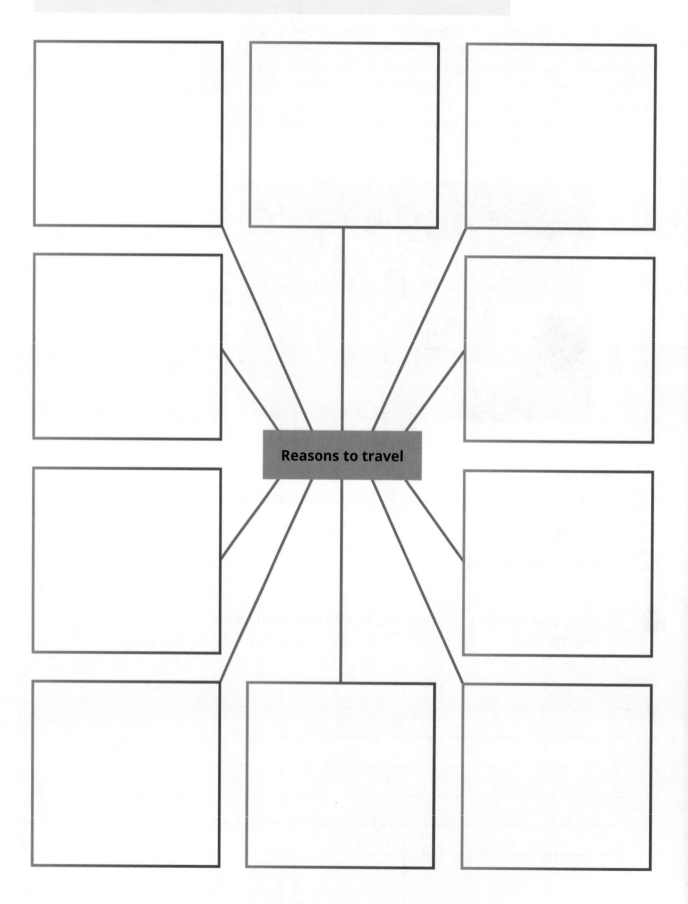

Reasons to travel

4   Look back at the information in your spider diagram about why people might travel. Now write about your own experiences. The questions below may help you with your writing.

Have you travelled? If you have, where did you travel to and from? Was it from one country to another? Or was it from one part of the country you live in to another?

If you haven't travelled, what do you think are the reasons? Would you like to travel? Where would you go to and why?

_____

_____

_____

_____

_____

_____

_____

_____

5   Our ancestors may have travelled long distances to new countries. Or they may have stayed in the countries they were born in. Think about your own heritage and answer the questions.

1   What countries might your family and relatives have travelled from and to? Do you know the reasons they travelled?

_____

_____

_____

_____

_____

2   Do you live in the country of your **heritage**? If not, what is the reason why? If you do, how does that make you feel?

_____

_____

_____

_____

6 Many people think travelling is an advantage to the human race. Others may not agree. Complete these activities to show your opinions.

1 Put the letters of these statements into the top row of the table.

A You gain new experiences.

B You learn about different cultures.

C It may be scary.

D You won't speak the language.

E You may make new friends abroad.

F You won't know anyone.

G You might get lost.

H There may be beautiful scenery.

I You could be promoting 'harmful tourism'.

J You might help to generate an income for the country you are visiting.

Advantages of travelling	Disadvantages of travelling

2 Add any other advantages or disadvantages of travelling you can think of to the table above.

7 **Migration** is when people move to another country to live. Complete the definition below by adding the correct words.

settle	moving	migration	intention

reasons	involuntary	length	voluntary

_____ is the act of _____ from one place in the world to another, across an international border, with the _____ to _____ permanently or temporarily. This term is used regardless of the move being _____ or _____ , the _____ for the movement or the _____ of the stay in the new location.

8 Read the text below. Do you agree or disagree with the quotation? Explain your answer.

The United Nations High Commissioner for Refugees (UNHCR) suggests that: 'The history of the world is such that everyone is a migrant.'

_____

_____

_____

_____

_____

_____

_____

In today's world, more people than ever live in a country that is different from the one they were born in. The United Nations states that, in 2019, the number of migrants globally reached about 272 million. This number is growing every year.

Some people are attracted to a new country for positive reasons, such as adventure. These are known as pull factors. Others may **have** to move even though they don't want to, perhaps to find work. These are known as push factors. Migration often happens as a result of both push and pull factors.

9 Match the push factor with the corresponding pull factor.

Push	**Pull**
lack of healthcare	political stability
lack of safety	better weather
drought	more wealth
high crime	better services
crop failure	higher employment
flooding	lower risk from natural hazards
war	fertile land
poverty	less crime

10   Look back at your answers to Activity 9. These are just
some of the push and pull factors causing global migration.
List some other reasons you can think of that may impact
someone's decision to migrate.

- _____
- _____
- _____
- _____
- _____
- _____

Push and pull factors often come under five main categories:

1   security

2   environment

3   stability

4   economics

5   services

11   Read the categories above. Then pick a matching pair of push
and pull factors from your answers to Activity 9. Select which
category the pair falls into and explain why you think the
factors would cause someone to migrate.

Push factor: _____

Pull factor: _____

Category: _____

_____

_____

_____

_____

Migrants are people who move from one country to another for reasons other than war and conflict.

Refugees are forced to leave their country to escape conflict, war or persecution.

Asylum seekers are forced to escape conflict, seeking protection and refuge within other countries.

Internally displaced people are forced to move within their own country to seek safety, perhaps due to environmental factors or local conflict (among other reasons).

12 Read the definitions above and write your own examples for each category.

Migrant	Refugee

Asylum seeker	Internally displaced person

13 How do you think travel or migration will impact your future? Explain your answer below and give examples.

_____

_____

_____

_____

_____

_____

_____

_____

_____

_____

_____

_____

_____

_____

What new things have you learned?

What had you not thought about before?

Global trade, ethics, production and consumption

Objective

GI8.3B – Knowledge about how global trade and economy works: how it benefits some people and is detrimental for others.

We will learn:

- what global trade is
- the main reasons for global trade
- the effects of global trade on others.

Key vocabulary

capital resource, commodity, export, fair trade, global economy, globalisation, human resource, imports, initiatives, natural resource, outsourcing, trade agreement

i Not all countries have everything they need, which means they must trade with other countries who can supply those things.

Very early in history, humans established trade routes with others by linking countries and communities across landscapes and bodies of waters. Products, ideas and cultures were shared and experienced through these trade routes. Economies were established by producing, trading and distributing goods and services. This has resulted in 'globalisation' and global trade, which is even more accessible today through improved travel and new technology. Air travel and cargo ships allow all bulky goods to travel around the world instantly, while information and communications technology (ICT) allows consumers and companies to communicate instantly. Even the remotest of places are now connected.

Throughout history, humans have traded with other humans. The most famous trade route was known as the Silk Road, which connected Asia to Europe. Other routes such as the spice route, incense route and salt route followed, each connecting different countries to resources they did not have.

Our connections with the world have grown over the centuries. We eat food from different cultures and we listen to music from around the world.

1 Think about your own life. What connections have you made with the rest of the world? What do you use that may have come from another part of the world? Add all of your ideas to the spider diagram.

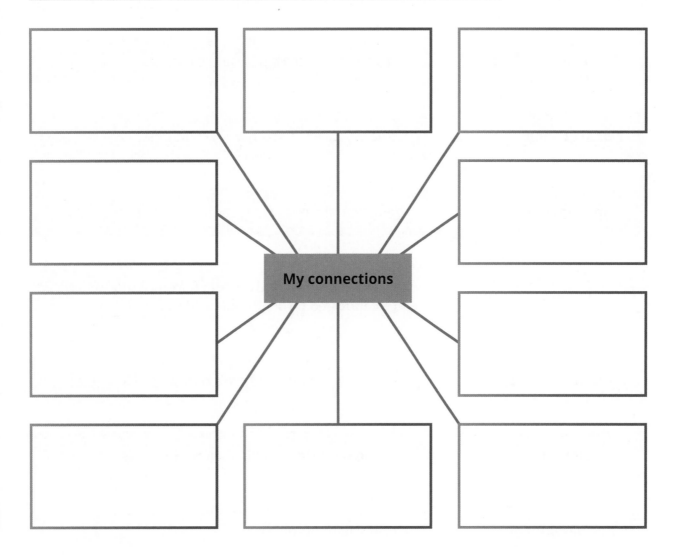

Trade can involve different parties making or sourcing products, goods or services to buy and sell to others.

2   Look at these key terms which are used to describe the trade process. Match each to its definition.

capital resource	The marketplace where countries compete to buy and sell products
commodity	Bringing something into a country to sell
export	Skills and techniques provided by people
global economy	A treaty between two or more countries
human resource	Produce that comes from earth and nature
import	The process by which the world becomes more interconnected through trade and travel
natural resource	Buildings, machines and tools used to produce goods
outsourcing	Sending products to other countries for sale
trade agreement	A useful item of value
globalisation	When you use a country or company that is not your own for part of your business, manufacturing or production

3 Choose **two** key terms from those listed in Activity 2 and create a picture for each term. This can be anything to help you remember the definition of the key term.

4 Using the vocabulary from Activity 2, write your own explanation of how global trade works.

_____

_____

_____

_____

_____

_____

_____

_____

If a country needs something it cannot produce itself, it must trade with another country. If the country relies on a product, money or service being supplied by another country, it becomes interdependent. Food is an excellent example of why many countries become interdependent on each other.

5 Think of the food you eat or have access to. Use the table to categorise this food into two groups.

Imported foods you could grow in your country	Imported foods you could not grow in your country

6 What do you think happens if a country refuses to trade?

_____

_____

_____

7 Think of a product – other than food – that you rely on. Does it come from another country? Can you only buy it from that country? Discuss your answers below.

_____

_____

_____

_____

_____

Some people believe that global connection has caused a weakening of culture. By connecting with other cultures and adopting parts of them, people may be losing their own identities. For example, some Indigenous groups now wear Western clothing.

8 Read the text above. Do you agree or disagree with this idea? Explain your answer below.

_____

_____

_____

Technology and social media have had a huge impact on trade today. There is a higher demand for produce and a greater need for profit. This has pushed companies to make products more cheaply and quickly. As a result, many companies now outsource work to other companies to satisfy this new demand.

9 Read the text above. Tick other reasons why you think companies outsource production.

☐ Increased efficiency   ☐ Expertise

☐ Space   ☐ To spend more money

☐ Cheap labour   ☐ To take over the world

☐ Cheaper materials   ☐ To become bankrupt

10 Look at your answers to Activity 9. Which reasons do you feel would **not** support a **fair trade** agreement? Explain why.

_____

_____

_____

_____

_____

Although there are many benefits of global trade, a lot of trade agreements are uneven and unequal. The world is split into two categories: more economically developed countries (MEDCs) and less economically developed countries (LEDCs).

11 Complete the diagram, using the key words below, to describe the types of trade you think would occur between MEDCs and LEDCs. Then answer the questions.

high-value trade   low-value trade   little to no trade

Global trade routes	Less economically developed country	More economically developed country
More economically developed country		
Less economically developed country		

1 Based on your completed diagram, what do you think is the impact of unequal trade between MEDCs and LEDCs?

_____

_____

_____

_____

_____

2 Is there anything we could do to improve this situation? Write your ideas below.

_____

_____

_____

_____

_____

12 Many companies outsource their production to LEDCs, even though their head offices may be located in MEDCs. Read this case study and then answer the questions that follow on the next page.

Jeans are a typical piece of clothing that many people own and wear. Dating back to the eighteenth century, hard-wearing denim material was used for a range of jobs, including mining and sailing. Jeans are now a modern-day fashion item that are sold for anywhere between around US $13 to more than US $800 for a designer pair.

The production of blue jeans is a good example of globalisation. In order to make a pair of denim jeans, you need cotton. Cotton grows in a subtropical climate and needs a minimum growing temperature of 15 degrees Celsius and a temperature of 30 degrees Celsius during the harvest season. It also requires an annual rainfall of 50 cm. This means that cotton is mainly grown in China, India, the USA, Pakistan, Brazil, Australia, Uzbekistan and Turkey.

From the farmer's field, cotton then travels to the factory. These factories are usually located in an LEDC due to cheap labour costs. This means companies do not have to pay high wages. Companies can produce jeans for a very low price and sell them at higher prices worldwide, making huge profits.

When the cotton arrives at the factory, people working long hours in dirty, cramped conditions turn the cotton into denim and produce a product we would recognise as a pair of jeans. Throughout this process, more products from around the world are added to the jeans, for example, threads, brass rivets, softer cotton for pockets and zips.

Once the jeans have been made, they travel from the factory to high streets around the world, sometimes using multiple modes of transport. By the time they get to shops, they have probably travelled thousands of miles.

However, not all factories produce clothing by exploiting cheap labour. Campaigns for change, that educate people on the impact of fast fashion, are having an impact. Many brands are now implementing **initiatives** that ensure that their denim is ethical and sustainable.

1   Look back at the case study on the previous page. Who benefits from this type of production? Explain your answer.

_____

_____

_____

_____

2   Who does not benefit from this type of production? Explain your answer.

_____

_____

_____

_____

3   What are some of the changes companies could bring about to make trade fairer?

_____

_____

_____

_____

_____

4   What could you do, as a consumer, to help bring about change?

_____

_____

_____

_____

_____

What new things have you learned?

What had you not thought about before?

Global wealth and poverty

Objective

GI8.3C – Ability to critique the work of organisations, initiatives, charities and **non-government organisations (NGOs)** whose aim is to alleviate poverty.

We will learn:

- how pictures can tell a thousand words
- the definition of poverty
- how organisations impact change
- to analyse the impact of charities on making change.

Key vocabulary

charities, impact, initiatives, non-government organisations (NGOs), organisations, poverty

The United Nations states that in 2015, 736 million people lived below the international poverty line. However, this figure decreased slightly due to the COVID-19 pandemic, with more than 71 million people being pushed into extreme poverty. Many organisations, **initiatives**, charities and NGOs aim to tackle global poverty through charitable donations. Although charitable donations are recognised as supporting needs, how effective could they be in tackling poverty specifically?

1 It is thought that 'a picture is worth a thousand words'. Look at the images below and answer the questions.

1 How do the images below make you feel? For example, what memories or thoughts and feelings do they provoke?

_____

_____

_____

2 Do these images make you want to do something, like dance or meet with friends? Add your thoughts to the boxes.

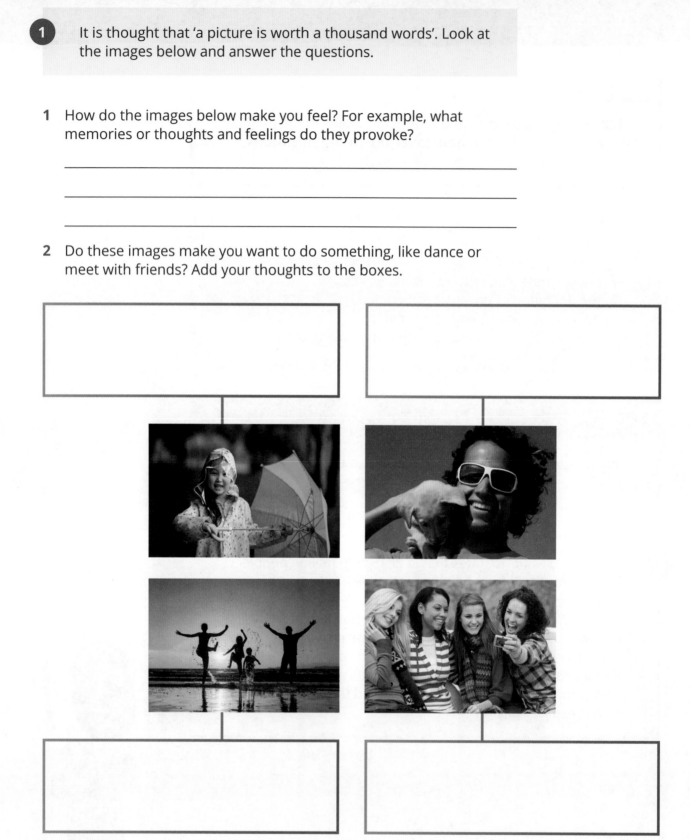

2   Now, look at these images and answer the questions.

1   How do these images make you feel? What are your thoughts and feelings for each one? Use the boxes to write them down.

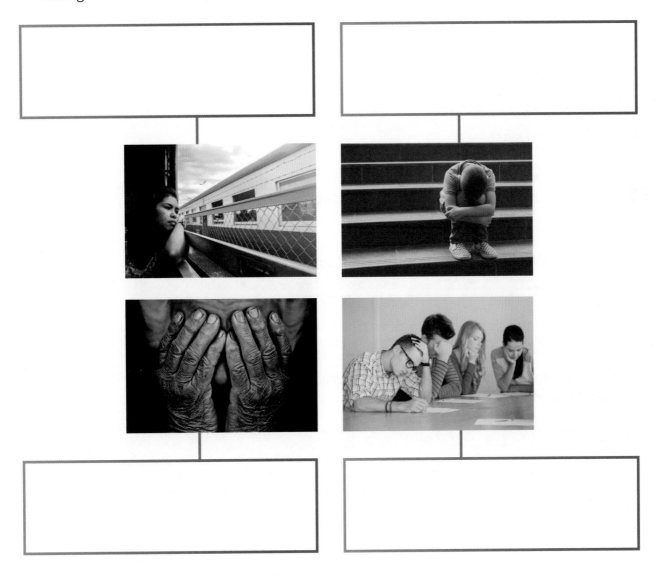

2   What diferent emotions do these images evoke compared to the previous pictures?

_____

_____

3   Why do you think images like these are used in advertising or for raising awareness?

_____

_____

_____

_____

3 Look at the list below. Tick all the indicators of someone in **poverty**.

☐ Lack of income

☐ Hunger and malnutrition

☐ Restricted access to education

☐ Limited access to healthcare

☐ Social discrimination

☐ Social exclusion

4 Look again at the list above and then answer these questions.

1 Did any of these indicators surprise you? If so, which ones?

_____

_____

_____

2 Can you think of any indicators that are missing from the list? Add them below.

- _____

- _____

- _____

- _____

5 Living in poverty can have many consequences in a person's life. Sort the list below based on whether you think each is a cause or consequence of poverty.

- Health problems
- Housing problems
- Unemployment and lack of jobs
- Low-level skills
- Committing crime

- High living costs
- Poor educational achievement
- Discrimination
- Homelessness
- Relationship and family problems

Causes	Consequences

6 Pick a cause from your completed table. Write a corresponding consequence and explain how the two may be interconnected.

_____

_____

_____

_____

7 Read the text and answer the questions below.

> Across the world, there are different levels of poverty. These range from destitution to living below the minimum income standard. Destitution means you can't afford to eat or stay clean, warm and dry. Living below the minimum income standard means you can just about get through each day financially. However, it's difficult to manage unexpected expenses and you live your life under pressure.

1 Do you think the media and **charities** portray poverty in an accurate way? Explain your answer below.

_____

_____

_____

_____

2 Why do you think the media and charities choose to portray poverty in this way?

_____

_____

_____

_____

> Charities are non-profitable **organisations** that aim to relieve an injustice in the world. To register as a charity, their objectives must be made clear. Their annual reports are made publicly available, making them fully accountable.

8 Some people believe that the biggest charities are successful due to favouritism rather than their area of need. Explain why you agree or disagree with this statement.

_____

_____

_____

_____

9 Name **four** charities you know. Identify their purpose and how they help to solve their chosen injustice.

Charity 1: _____

Purpose: _____

_____

How they solve injustice: _____

_____

Charity 2: _____

Purpose: _____

_____

How they solve injustice: _____

_____

Charity 3: _____

Purpose: _____

_____

How they solve injustice: _____

_____

Charity 4: _____

Purpose: _____

_____

How they solve injustice: _____

_____

10 Charities focus on raising money and awareness for injustices in the world. Write one or two sentences describing why raising money might be a good solution to solving injustices.

_____

_____

_____

_____

_____

Some people think that raising money to fight poverty is a way of simply accepting the problem, and therefore the need to fix the root of the problem is reduced.

11 Read the statement above and then write two arguments: one for it, and one against it. Discuss the **impact** each side of the argument would have.

For	Against

'The starfish' by Loren Eiseley

One day a man was walking along the beach when he noticed a boy picking something up and gently throwing it into the ocean.

Approaching the boy, he asked, 'What are you doing?'

The youth replied, 'Throwing starfish back into the ocean. The surf is up and the tide is going out. If I don't throw them back, they'll die.'

'Son,' the man said, 'don't you realise there are miles and miles of beach and hundreds of starfish? You can't make a difference!'

After listening politely, the boy bent down, picked up another starfish and threw it back into the surf.

Then, smiling at the man, he said, 'I made a difference for that one.'

12   Read the story above and answer the questions.

1   How might this story be used as an analogy for how charities operate?

_____

_____

_____

_____

2   In the story, the boy is helping one starfish at a time. Do you think this would be a more effective strategy towards the poverty crisis?

_____

_____

_____

_____

If we raise money to fix a problem in 10 years' time and make the world a better place to live in then, we wouldn't be helping someone in poverty right now.

13 Read the statement above and then list the advantages and disadvantages of waiting to fix a problem rather than acting now.

Advantages: _____

_____

_____

_____

Disadvantages: _____

_____

_____

_____

Efforts that are going into charity should really go into changing government policies.

14 Read the statement above and say why someone might agree with it and why someone might disagree with it.

Agree: _____

_____

_____

_____

Disagree: _____

_____

_____

_____

15 Based on what you have learned in this session, think about an effective way to solve global poverty. Use the space below to discuss ideas, or to create a plan or poster for how you would achieve this.

What new things have you learned?

What had you not thought about before?

Information, technology and communication

Objective

GI8.3D – Knowledge about the power and influence of the media and its ability to shape people's lives.

We will learn:

- about the role of the media
- about different types of influence
- about the impact the media can have on your life.

Key vocabulary

advertising, benefit, impact, influences, media, misinformation, negative, politics, positive

i Throughout your life you will have been, and will continue to be, influenced by many people, including your peers, family, community, colleagues and possibly others.

As technology advances and communications around the world strengthen, the influence from what we see and hear from others deepens. Having the world at your fingertips through mobile devices and computers means you can receive world news updates in seconds. Advertisements are tailored to your likes and dislikes through social media platforms.

The audience for influencers just became global.

1   List the biggest **influences** in your life to date.

- _____
- _____
- _____
- _____
- _____

2   Match the words to their definitions.

media		An announcement to the public promoting a product, service or event
influencer		To have an effect on someone or something
advertisement		A collective name for the means of communicating to the world
impact		Someone or something that has an effect on another person's opinions, feelings or behaviour

3 Think about why we use the **media**. Rank the reasons by adding them to the diamond grid, with the most important at the top and least important at the bottom.

education	staying in touch with friends and family	staying up to date with news and current events
networking	**politics**	entertainment
seeing what others are doing	researching new products or ideas	sharing your point of view

4 List any other reasons you can think of to add to the diamond grid.

- _____
- _____
- _____
- _____

5 Complete the spider diagram with all the media platforms you have access to in your day-to-day life. Then answer the questions.

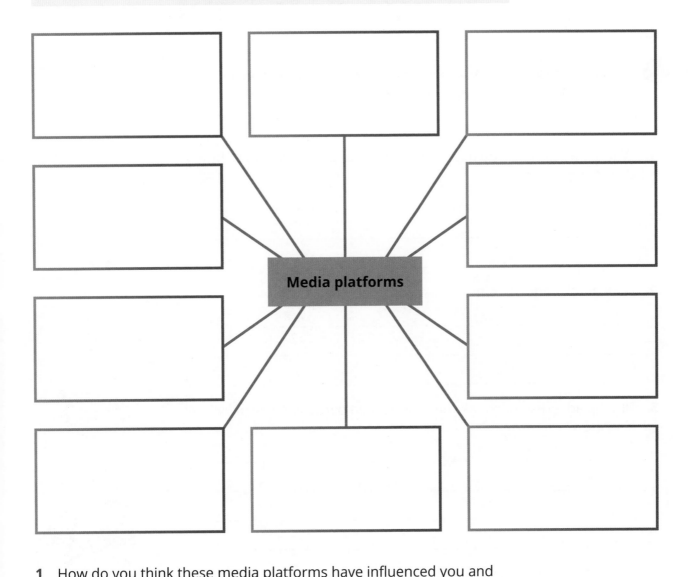

1 How do you think these media platforms have influenced you and your decisions, behaviours or opinions?

_____

_____

_____

_____

2 Do you feel one media platform has influenced you more than any others? Why do you think this is?

_____

_____

_____

_____

The media can influence people in a variety of ways, including how we live and behave. One way this can happen is through the use of advertisements.

6   Think of a food advertisement you have seen recently on any media platform and then answer the questions.

1   What strategies did the manufacturer use to persuade you to buy this food product?

_____

_____

_____

2   How did the advertisement make you feel? Explain why.

_____

_____

_____

3   Did the advertisement link the product to a particular way of living? If so, how?

_____

_____

_____

_____

4   What message did this advertisement send about what children, teenagers and adults should be like?

_____

_____

_____

_____

The media is where most people get their information regarding political and social decisions. People can decide whether to accept the information they have heard or to reject it and form their own opinions.

The media can influence the public in different ways, some having a **positive** impact and others having a **negative** impact.

7   Sort the statements into positive or negative influences.

- Gives stereotypical views of how we should behave

- Suggests eating junk food is cool

- Presents unrealistic body images

- Educates on new topics

- Offers biased views on situations

- Develops unrealistic views of other people's lives

- Gives inspiration for looks

- Promotes a perception of what normal should look like

- Allows self expression

- Gives inspiration for lifestyles

- Raises awareness of health

- Instils wrong perceptions of lifestyles

- Provides instant understanding of current affairs

- Develops beliefs in biased views or stories

Positive influence	Negative influence

8   Choose **one** of the statements from Activity 7 and discuss why you believe it is a positive or negative influence of the media.

_____

_____

_____

_____

_____

_____

One major negative influence from media platforms is fake news. These are stories that contain deliberate **misinformation**. Fake news can be spread through print, news media and social media.

9   Tick the reasons why you think media platforms use fake news.

☐   To cast doubt on legitimate news stories

☐   To make up stories that would benefit others

☐   To make up stories in order to share awareness of a product (**advertising** strategy)

☐   To score high ratings

☐   To communicate to a wider audience

10   Choose **one** reason and explain why you ticked it.

_____

_____

_____

_____

_____

_____

11   'Media companies should **benefit** from the distribution of fake news.'

Discuss whether you agree or disagree with this statement and explain why.

_____

_____

_____

_____

12   Imagine you have found a website that states something different to what you already know. This might be fake news. Discuss what you could do in this situation.

_____

_____

_____

_____

_____

13   List some negative influences of the media and then suggest a safer approach for them that promotes well-being.

Potential negative influences of the media	Solutions to promote well-being

In today's world, the media plays a vital role in informing people about global and local politics and current affairs, among other things. Politicians and leaders are held accountable by the public for their actions.

14   Read the text above and then say what you think might happen if there was no longer any media.

_____

_____

_____

_____

_____

Influence is not just achieved through the media. You are an influencer within your networks with family, peers, community and social media.

15   Read the text above and then describe how you could help keep others safe and knowledgeable regarding the influence of the media.

_____

_____

_____

_____

_____

_____

What new things have you learned?
What had you not thought about before?

Global health, food and well-being

Objective

GI8.3E – Understand the benefits of, and problems with, the global distribution of medicines.

We will learn:

- about the pharmaceutical industry
- about the process of making medicines
- of the impact of patents on companies and individuals.

Key vocabulary

government, healthcare, industry, medicine development, patents, pharmaceutical, supply chain, trials

i

The pharmaceutical industry is thought to have developed in the nineteenth century when people believed animals, minerals and plants contained medicinal properties. Our understanding of basic **medicine development** was the result of centuries of trial and error, along with the application of chemistry and physics.

Modern pharmaceutical industries are now able to identify new techniques in medicine development. This continual progression is fundamental to the control and elimination of disease around the world. However, the distribution of these medicines is not always equal.

A **healthcare** system is something that is set up to look after the health needs of a country, an area, or perhaps a particular population. All healthcare systems aim to provide care and medicine for the sick. Sometimes the care and medicine is free, and sometimes it isn't. There may even be places in the world where the majority of citizens don't have access to the healthcare system and medicines at all.

1 Read the text above and in the introduction to this session. Then answer the questions.

1 Name **three** structures, for instance a family doctor's practice, that are part of a healthcare system.

1 _____

2 _____

3 _____

2 Why is your health so important?

_____

_____

_____

3 What happens when you become ill? What do you do?

_____

_____

_____

4 What medicines do you have access to through your healthcare system?

_____

_____

5 Are there any medicines you may not have access to? Why do you think this is?

_____

_____

_____

The **pharmaceutical industry** involves the research, development and manufacture of medication by private and public organisations. There are many stages involved with getting a medicine from the pharmaceutical company to the patient. The whole procedure is known as a supply chain.

2 Label each stage of the pharmaceutical **supply chain** using the headings given.

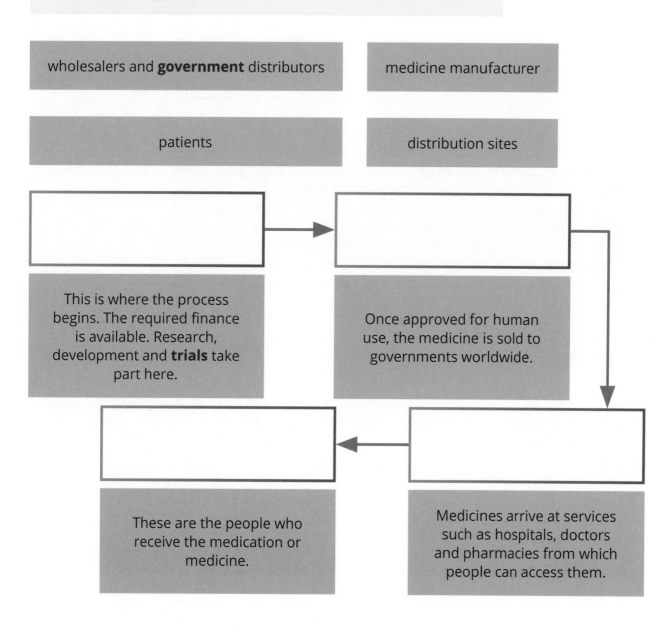

wholesalers and **government** distributors

medicine manufacturer

patients

distribution sites

This is where the process begins. The required finance is available. Research, development and **trials** take part here.

Once approved for human use, the medicine is sold to governments worldwide.

These are the people who receive the medication or medicine.

Medicines arrive at services such as hospitals, doctors and pharmacies from which people can access them.

The World Health Organization (WHO) states that 2 billion people in the world do not have access to medicines, and 80 per cent of the world's population live with no, or very little, access to moderate or severe pain relief.

3 Read the text above. Suggest why there might be such large inequalities with the distribution of medicines globally.

_____

_____

_____

The pharmaceutical industry is based on research and development. It maintains interest from researchers because it uses patents. Patents are pieces of legislation that give inventors exclusive rights to what they are making. This stops anyone else from making, using, selling or importing a product or process included in the patented invention. Patents are used in a variety of industries.

4 Read the text about patents above and then answer these questions.

1 List some inventions you use. Which ones do you think are patented? Tick them.

☐ _____ ☐ _____

☐ _____ ☐ _____

☐ _____ ☐ _____

2 How do you think patents link to the pharmaceutical industry?

_____

_____

_____

_____

Patents have been used to encourage research and development. However, countries without economical means are unable to buy patents, meaning that research and development into the health needs of these countries is halted.

5   Read the text above and then answer these questions.

1   What impact do you think not being able to buy patents has on the distribution of medicines worldwide?

_____

_____

_____

2   Do you think not being able to buy patents is fair? Explain your answer.

_____

_____

_____

A generic drug is made in exactly the same way as the patented drug, but is only allowed for sale after the patent expires.

6   Discuss with a Talk Partner whether certain drugs, for example vaccines, should never be patented.

The pharmaceutical industry is a business and can involve multinational companies. This means there is a delicate balance between health and money. If pharmaceutical companies care more about profits than health, then it can have disastrous life-and-death consequences. However, the pharmaceutical industry is a business, not a charity. So when sales from new medicines do not provide a profit, companies stop researching and investing.

Developing new medicines can be a risky investment. Out of all the medicines that are researched and developed, only a small number prove to be effective. Most others are judged to be ineffective. Or it could be that the negative side effects of the medicine outweigh the benefits.

Despite hundreds of clinical trials and costing millions of dollars to produce, the majority of new medicines never make it to the public. Companies that have invested greatly into the production of new medicines suffer huge financial losses. If a pharmaceutical company produces a successful and marketable medicine, it will have to increase the retail price to compensate for all the other unsuccessful medicine trials it has lost money on. This often means that the price of the medicine can be very expensive.

In addition, the process would have been patented, which typically lasts for 20 years. During these 20 years, the pharmaceutical company must research, develop and manufacture the medicine, which generally takes 10 years. This only leaves 10 years to make a profit before the patent runs out, after which other companies can then sell the product at a fraction of the price.

7   Read the text above and then answer the questions.

1   Why is the production of medicine so expensive?

_____

_____

_____

_____

2   In what way do you think the production cost could be reduced?

_____

_____

_____

_____

8   Many medicines on the market today sell for very different prices. Rank these medicines from least to most expensive to buy as a patient.

medication for cancer   paracetamol   insulin

HIV or AIDS medication   antibiotics   vaccines

least expensive

_____

_____

_____

_____

_____

_____

most expensive

9   Explain why you placed the medicines in Activity 8 in the order that you did.

_____

_____

_____

_____

_____

_____

Medicine is expensive and some people may depend on it for the rest of their lives.

10 Read the statement above. Then say whether you think it is fair for someone to pay for medication if it is a necessity for living. Why or why not?

_____

_____

_____

_____

In order for families in poorer countries to afford medicines, they sometimes have to sell their belongings. This, in turn, can push them further into poverty.

11 Imagine you are in charge of the production of medicine in a country. You must ensure that everyone has fair and equal access to the medications they need. However, you must also ensure the pharmaceutical industry stays successful. Explain how you would do this.

_____

_____

_____

_____

_____

_____

_____

What new things have you learned?

What had you not thought about before?

Understanding rights

Objective

HR8.5A – Knowledge that some issues concerning rights are **contested**.

We will learn:

- about freedom of expression and its limitations
- about the agreed articles of human rights
- about the legal frameworks in place to support human rights.

Key vocabulary

contested, expression, freedom, human, rights, United Nations

Do you feel as though you can express your opinions? If you didn't agree with a decision made by someone in a position of authority, do you think you could openly criticise it? Can you use your voice or other forms of communication to share your thoughts and feelings with others?

Without people standing up for their rights and supporting the rights of others, there would be no progress and no successes in the fight for human rights.

1   Think about some of the ways people can choose to express themselves. Create a spider diagram in the space below and include as many ideas as possible.

Think beyond your own experiences. How might people in different countries express themselves? How might people of different genders and different ages choose to express themselves?

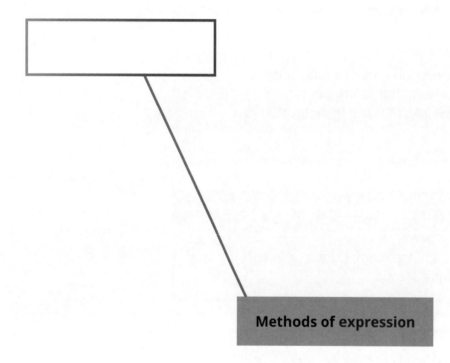

Methods of expression

After the Second World War, when millions of people had lost their lives and millions more had been driven from their homes, the leaders of the world got together and set up the **United Nations**. They did this to help stop wars between countries and build a better world through unity. The United Nations drew up a list of 30 **human** rights that belong to everyone in the world: the Universal Declaration of Human Rights (UDHR). The world's governments promised to tell everyone about these **rights** and to protect them.

2 Below are just some of the rights that have been agreed by the world's government leaders. Tick the ones you think are a part of the Universal Declaration of Human Rights.

- ☐ All born free and equal
- ☐ Right to own property
- ☐ Right to own a dog
- ☐ Right to life
- ☐ Right to privacy
- ☐ **Freedom** from slavery and torture
- ☐ Right to work
- ☐ Freedom to record anyone without permission
- ☐ Right to adequate standard of living
- ☐ Right to a television in your home
- ☐ Right to marry
- ☐ Right to equality before the law

- ☐ Freedom from discrimination
- ☐ Freedom of assembly and association
- ☐ Right to change hair colour
- ☐ Freedom of opinion and expression
- ☐ Right to own gaming device
- ☐ Right to nationality
- ☐ Right to rest and leisure
- ☐ Freedom to take money from others when you are without
- ☐ Freedom to sell others' belongings for personal profit

Some of the rights protected by the UDHR are considered to be 'absolute', meaning that under no circumstance can they be interfered with. Others are classified as 'limited', which means they can be restricted in some specific situations.

3 Decide whether you think the human rights listed below are absolute or limited. Then complete the table.

Freedom from slavery and forced labour

Right to participate in free elections

Freedom of expression

Freedom of assembly and association

Right to liberty

Protection from discrimination

Freedom from torture and inhuman or degrading treatment

Right to peaceful enjoyment of your property

Right to education

Right to marry

Right to life

Absolute	Limited

4   Looking back at Activity 3, explain your choice of 'absolute' rights.

_____

_____

_____

_____

_____

_____

5   Say if you agree (or not) that some human rights can be restricted and considered as 'limited'. Give your reasons.

_____

_____

_____

_____

_____

6   List some potential circumstances or situations that would mean particular rights are considered 'limited'.

- _____
- _____
- _____
- _____
- _____
- _____
- _____

7   Select **nine** of the human rights listed in Activity 3 and arrange them into the diamond grid below. Place the most basic rights at the very top and the rest according to their significance. Even though your diamond ranking may vary from others, it is important you decide on an arrangement you see as true and can give reasons for it.

8 Look at the human right you put at the top of your diamond ranking in Activity 7. Why do you believe this to be the most basic human right of all? Use the questions and prompts in the planning box to help organise your response. Then explain your thinking on the lines below.

What is the importance of this human right?

What are some of the risks involved with not having it met or adhered to?

What would happen if we did not have it?

---

9 Freedom of expression is also fulfilled through your right to express yourself freely. Match these types of expression to the examples. Some of the expressions can be used more than once, and some of the examples may match to more than one expression.

Journalist criticising a monarchy in a newspaper

Interpretive dance about climate change

published articles or leaflets

Painting about equal rights

television or radio broadcasting

Someone posting on social media about their government

books and literature

the internet and websites

Starting a hashtag in support of a human rights movement

works of art

Author writing about their personal experience in another country

social media

Someone giving their view on new tax laws via interview with news network

Sharing information with voters about candidate in upcoming election

Censorship is the supervision and control of the information and ideas circulated in society, usually in the media. It occurs when individuals or groups alter or suppress speech, writing and images that they find objectionable or dangerous.

10 Think of some ways in which censorship might be used to interfere with a magazine or newspaper's freedom of expression. Create your own spider diagram and add your ideas to it.

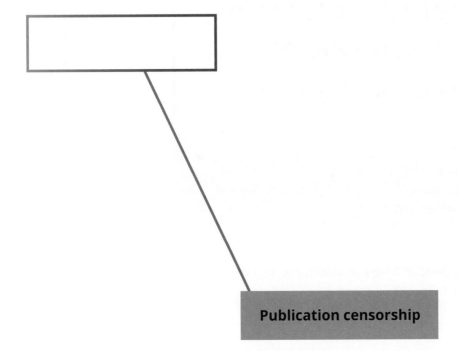

Publication censorship

Read the text and newspaper headline below and then answer the questions.

Laws help to make human rights a reality in people's lives. For example, a government who says it will respect human rights must then do so by law. If they don't, a court can hold that government to account.

Human rights laws stop people from taking photos in public parks

A former newsreader has criticised a local council after he was banned from taking photographs of flowers in public parks – in case it infringed people's human rights.

1 How might the newspaper headline be misleading to its readers with regards to human rights?

_____

_____

_____

2 What does the headline suggest people are taking photographs of?

_____

_____

_____

_____

3 What does finding out more about the context of the photographs suggest about the intention behind the newspaper headline?

_____

_____

_____

_____

The United Declaration of Human Rights (UDHR) is a momentous document in the history of human rights. It was drafted by representatives with different legal and cultural backgrounds, from all regions of the world, and was proclaimed as a common standard of achievements for all peoples across all nations. It established a collection of 30 fundamental human rights to be universally protected, which are referred to as 'Articles'.

12 Use the words below to complete the summarising statements about the UDHR.

where	free	fairly	safe	believe

protected	humiliate	torture	who

We are born _____ and equal, and should treat others in the same way.

We have all these rights in the Declaration, no matter

_____ we are, _____ we're from or

what we _____ in.

We have the right to life, and to be free and feel _____ .

Nobody has any right to hurt, _____ or

_____ us.

Everyone has the right to be _____ by the law. The law is the same for everyone. It must treat us all

_____ .

We can all ask for the law to help us when we are not treated fairly.

13   Suggest the kinds of issues and possible conflicts people may have experienced before the rights protected by the UDHR were agreed.

_____

_____

_____

_____

_____

_____

_____

14   Choose **one** of the issues or conflicts you mentioned above and explain how the UDHR would seek to improve this.

_____

_____

_____

_____

_____

_____

What new things have you learned?

What had you not thought about before?

Violation of rights (Greater Depth)

Objective

HR8.5B – Knowledge of rights violations in the past and the ongoing implications and resulting injustice in societies today.

We will learn:

- about the implications of rights violations
- how rights violations and discrimination in the past have had long-term impacts
- about historical rights violations that resulted in injustice in societies today.

Key vocabulary

discrimination, human, rights, violation

Have you ever had something you owned taken away from you? What was the value of the thing that was taken from you? How did you feel when it was taken from you? Were you able to reclaim it?

Human rights belong to everyone. There are no conditions. There are no circumstances that determine whether you have them or not. No one should be allowed to interfere or take them away from you. To break or act against something, especially a law or an agreement such as the United Declaration of Human Rights (UDHR), is called a 'violation'.

The UDHR outlines the human rights all people are entitled to. In the event that these rights are not protected or disregarded, they are violated.

1 Give an example for each of the settings below in which your rights are protected.

When you are in the workplace

_____

_____

When you use public healthcare services

_____

_____

When you access education

_____

_____

When you use transport

_____

_____

When you join a club or association

_____

_____

2 Choose **one** of the settings above and then answer the questions.

Situation: _____

1 Who might violate your rights in this setting? How?

_____

_____

_____

2 Can you think of any ways this **violation** might be rectified and who by? List them.

- _____

- _____

- _____

Article 10 of the UDHR protects your right to hold your own opinions and to express them freely without government interference. This includes the right to express your views aloud for example, through public protest and demonstrations.

3 Think of **four** protests that have occurred in the past. For each one, suggest the cause or reason why people were protesting.

Protest/Demonstration	Cause/Reason

4 Choose a cause you have, or would, support through protest or demonstration. Explain why you chose this cause.

Cause: _____

_____

_____

_____

5 Explain why you might encourage others to exercise their freedom of expression through protest or demonstration.

_____

_____

_____

6 Read the text below and then answer the questions on this and the following page.

Your rights must be protected when you have contact with public bodies such as your local council or government departments. There are also situations where a public authority has a duty to stop exploitation of rights by an individual or company. Read what happened to Mike...

Mike lives in London, in the United Kingdom. He has been stopped and searched more than 30 times by the police while driving his car or when he's out for a run in his own neighbourhood. Each time he is approached and informally questioned by officers, it is done in a very public manner. He feels the reason for this is to humiliate and embarrass him. Eventually, though, he is always told he is free to go, because he hasn't actually done anything. Mike believes he is a target due to the colour of his skin. He thinks this unfair, disproportionate targeting of certain ethnic minorities is degrading and is a violation of his rights.

1 Do you think Mike is right to feel that he is being targeted by the police? Give your reasons.

_____

_____

_____

_____

2 What rights are being violated by the police when they carry out unsolicited stop and search procedures? Tick all that apply.

☐ Freedom of opinion and information

☐ Freedom from torture and inhuman or degrading treatment

☐ Protection from **discrimination**

☐ Freedom of movement

3 Which **one** of the above do you think applies to Mike's situation? Explain why.

_____

_____

_____

_____

4 What do you think explains the police's treatment of Mike and other people who look like him?

_____

_____

_____

5 What actions could Mike take to stop this violation and ensure his rights, and potentially those of others, are protected?

_____

_____

_____

_____

_____

6 Who should take responsibility for ending this type of violation? How could they show their intention to end it?

_____

_____

_____

_____

7 What do you suggest can be done to stop individuals belonging to certain groups being disproportionately targeted and mistreated?

_____

_____

_____

_____

_____

Violations of rights come in many forms. Therefore, it is important that people are aware of their rights. They should also know what it might look like when someone tries to mistreat or deny them any of their rights. Discrimination is a rather large part of this and can present itself in different ways.

7 Match the four main types of discrimination people may suffer to its correct definition.

direct discrimination

Unwelcome treatment of any kind that violates your dignity or creates a hostile, degrading, humiliating or offensive environment. This can range from repeatedly mocking a worker's accent to psychologically intimidating employees by making threats or displaying discriminatory symbols.

indirect discrimination

Putting a rule, policy or system in place that has a worse impact on an individual with a protected characteristic than someone without one. For example, the housing department plans to redevelop some of its properties. Consultation events are held in the evenings, when many of the female residents are unable to attend due to childcare responsibilities.

victimisation

Treating one individual worse than another because of a protected characteristic. For example, an employer doesn't tell older, but still eligible and qualified, candidates about a promotion because they believe that people's memories get worse as they get older. This denies fair opportunities for all and prevents progression for those employees viewed as past their optimal age.

harassment

Treating someone poorly because they have made or are involved in a complaint of discrimination or harassment. For example, playing tricks on someone in the workplace because they have given evidence in relation to a claim being looked into.

8   Group these scenarios based on whether you think they are violations of rights or not.

| Drawing graffiti on images of a co-worker | Giving a friend a hug when they're upset | Spreading malicious rumours |

| Receiving flowers from colleagues on your birthday | Female employer commenting on a male employee's figure | Using racial slurs when referring to someone of another ethnicity |

| Informing all employees of upcoming promotions | Writing slanderous posts or comments on social media | Inviting only men in the office to a golf club |

| Denying someone training or promotion opportunities | Providing ramp access to buildings for wheelchair users | Retelling racist or sexist jokes from sitcoms/ comedy sketches |

Violation of rights	Not a violation of rights

9 Read Paulina's story to learn how she took action to ensure that the rights laws in her country actually served her.

Rights laws can be used to ensure an improved quality of life where the individual is unable to thrive in the current situation, as Paulina's story shows...

Paulina has a lifelong medical condition called multiple sclerosis (MS). She has been declared as severely physically disabled. Due to her MS, Paulina is confined to bed for most of the day. She requires constant care and assistance to complete seemingly 'basic' tasks such as pouring a drink and taking a shower. Paulina's local government authority said they could only provide her with a 45-minute care slot each day. This was just about enough time for her to be taken to the toilet and given a bath, and not much else. This meant that she was forced to spend the rest of her time alone, in bed.

Due to the ongoing low level of care allocated to her by the local authority, Paulina decided to find out if she could do something about it. She discovered that the rights laws in her country protected her, and that the treatment of someone with needs such as hers was unacceptable. Once she knew what rights she was entitled to, she used this information to take legal action to gain the support she required for an improved quality of life.

10 Refer back to the list of rights on page 202. Identify which of Paulina's rights were not being protected and which rights laws could be used to correct and counteract the mistreatment. Write down your ideas in the planning box below.

11 Choose **four** rights from page 202 that you believe were not protected in Paulina's story. Using your planning from Activity 9, complete the diagram below by identifying the rights that were violated and what you think could be done to counteract the violation.

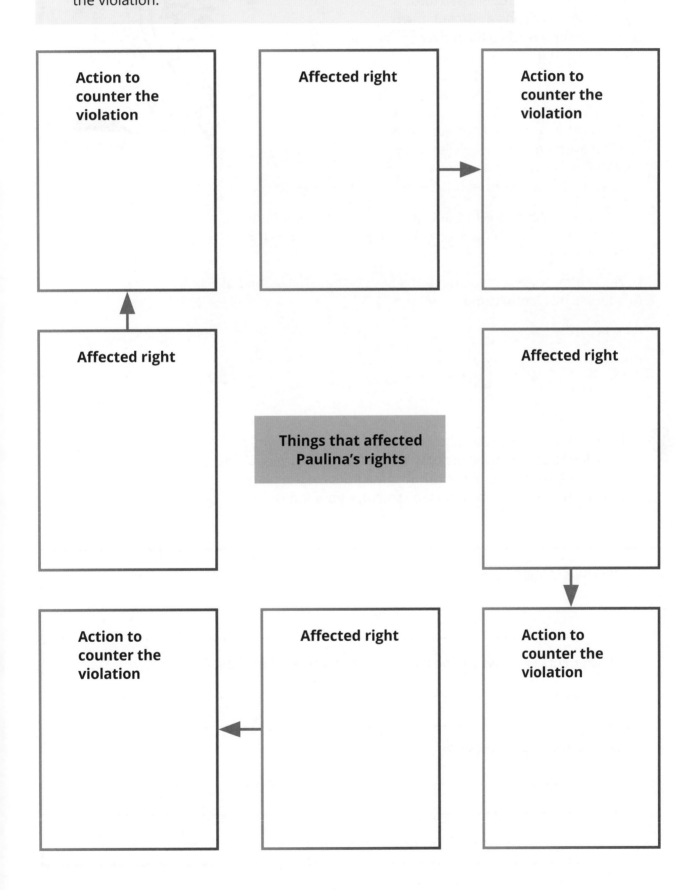

Action to counter the violation

Affected right

Action to counter the violation

Affected right

Affected right

Things that affected Paulina's rights

Action to counter the violation

Affected right

Action to counter the violation

Dear friend,

My name is Kaz and I am hoping you might have some advice.

I am a 13-year-old student at a local school. My school has a strict uniform policy and, as a result, I have been told that I'm not allowed to wear my jilbab. I have tried explaining that, because of my culture and religion, it is really important that I wear my jilbab and still respectfully wear the uniform just like everyone else. However, they continue to refuse to let me wear it. I've enclosed a photo of me wearing one for your reference.

I really don't think this is fair but I just don't know what to do anymore. It's awful because I feel as though I'm being dismissed because of my age.

I'd really appreciate it if you have any advice at all that I could use to address this issue further.

Kind regards,

Kaz

---

12 Read the letter from Kaz above. You are going to use your knowledge of human rights to write a letter of advice back to her on the next page. Write down some notes in the planning box below, using the prompts to structure your ideas.

Which right/rights are not being protected?

_____

_____

Which rights law/laws can be used to help to protect her rights?

_____

_____

What actions can Kaz take?

_____

_____

_____

Dear Kaz,

_____

_____

_____

_____

_____

_____

_____

_____

_____

_____

_____

_____

_____

_____

_____

_____

_____

_____

_____

_____

_____

Human rights belong to everyone, and each right is important and necessary for human beings to survive and thrive.

13 Imagine you are a natural historian. Use the four headings below to describe to an alien what human beings need in order to live and grow. You can write your descriptions, or draw and label them.

What do human beings need to survive?	**What things help us to grow physically?**

What things help us to succeed in life?	**What things put our ability to survive and thrive at risk?**

All human beings require the same basic needs to allow them to live and grow, and to be human. Each one of us has the right to have these needs fulfilled. 'Needs' are different from 'wants'. 'Wants' are things we desire because they may make us happy. However, they are not required to survive, grow and develop.

14 Read the text above and look at the list of needs and wants below. Then prioritise the list, based on a specific perspective. For example, you could choose age, gender or social class. Your chosen perspective will affect how you prioritise the list. Make a note of it in the box at the bottom.

Number your priorities, with 1 being the highest priority.

Nutritious food ☐	Designer accessories ☐	Education ☐
Mobile phone ☐	Meals out at restaurants ☐	Water ☐
Cosmetic surgery ☐	Protection from harm ☐	Shelter ☐
Employment ☐	Vehicles to get to places ☐	Privacy ☐
Healthcare ☐	Gadgets and game consoles ☐	Clothes ☐
Snacks and sweets ☐	Toys and games for entertainment ☐	Make-up ☐

My chosen perspective is...

15 Using your prioritised list from Activity 14, add the needs and wants to the appropriate sections of the diagram below.

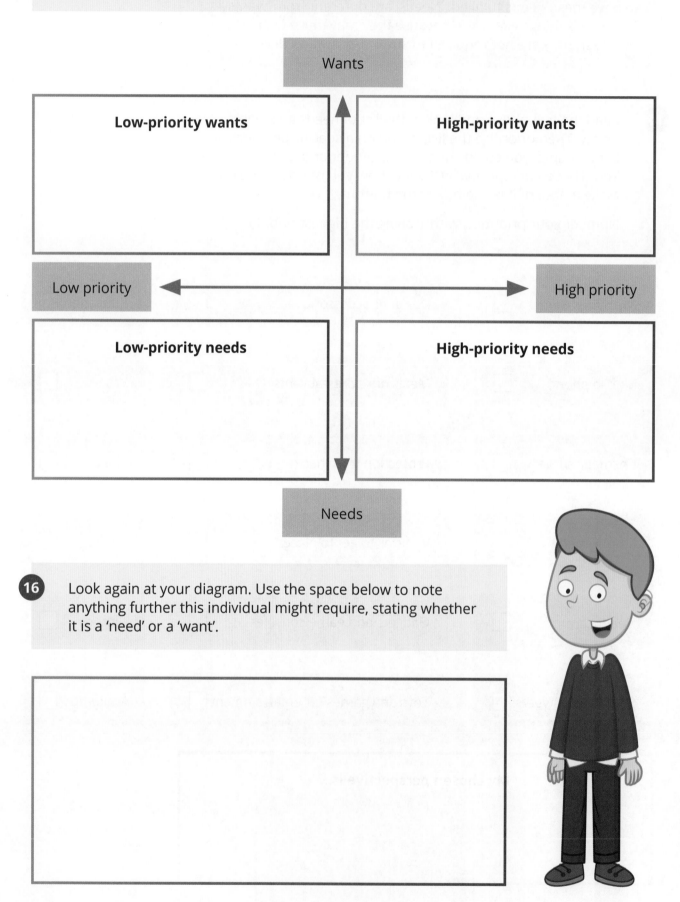

16 Look again at your diagram. Use the space below to note anything further this individual might require, stating whether it is a 'need' or a 'want'.

17 Complete these three statements about rights by underlining one of the options provided.

1 Human rights are the basic rights and **consequences/freedoms/ restrictions** that belong to every person in the world, from birth throughout their entire existence.

2 Although they can never be taken away, rights can sometimes be **suspended/bought**, for example if a person breaks the law, or in the interests of national security.

3 The basic rights outlined by the UDHR are based on a set of agreed and shared values like dignity, fairness, equality and respect. These values are defined and protected by **the individual/the law/ the police**.

18 Briefly describe how a person who has experienced discrimination and rights violations in the past may still feel the effects today.

_____

_____

_____

_____

_____

_____

_____

What new things have you learned?
What had you not thought about before?

Refugees, asylum seekers and internally displaced people

Objective

HR8.5C – Know about the work of the United Nations High Commissioner for Refugees (UNHCR).

We will learn:

- the definitions and differences between refugees, asylum seekers and internally displaced people
- how the UNHCR protects the rights of displaced persons
- what the UNHCR does to support displaced persons.

Key vocabulary

asylum seeker, internally displaced, refugee, rights, United Nations, United Nations High Commissioner for Refugees (UNHCR)

How important is your home to you? How important is your community to you? How important is your country to you? How important is your language to you? How important is your nationality to you? All of these are essential factors that contribute to our identity and make us who we are today. It is agreed, all over the world, that you have a right to each of these things.

So can you imagine if, one day, these birth-given rights were taken away from you or you had to sacrifice them in order to maintain a basic right – safety? Unfortunately, this is the case for many people around the world who have been forced to flee their country of origin because they are either escaping conflict or seeking international protection. The United Nations High Commissioner for Refugees (UNHCR) is responsible for safeguarding the rights of these people.

Imagine being forced to flee your home country in order to protect yourself and your family, and escape to safety. If you were lucky, you might have had time to pack a bag. If not, you would suddenly have to drop everything and run.

1 Read the scenario above and then complete the table with your thoughts.

What kind of event might cause someone to leave like this?	
Put yourself in the shoes of someone who this has happened to. What would this be like? How might you feel before leaving your home country? How might you feel after?	
When you eventually arrive in another country, what might be challenging for you at this time?	
What support do you hope will be available to you in this new country?	

2 Tick to show whether the statements below are true or false based on your understanding of refugees.

	True	False
A **refugee** is someone who has been forced to flee their country in order to escape war, persecution or natural disaster.		
Only adults over the age of 18 can be classed as refugees; children don't count.		
You can be a refugee in your own country.		
To be considered a refugee, you have to have crossed at least one border into another country.		
Refugees pack up all of their belongings and get them shipped to their destination country.		
It is unsafe for refugees to return to their home countries.		
Refugees always get to leave their home country with their families and loved ones.		
Refugees are only people from African countries.		
People from European countries can be refugees.		

3 Choose **two** of the statements you decided were false. Explain your reasons.

1 _____

_____

_____

2 _____

_____

_____

The word 'refugee' is regularly used as an umbrella term for people displaced by war, violence or persecution. However, there are different types of displaced people, each with a set of characteristics that come with specific needs. Understanding how to differentiate these is important and will contribute to better understanding of this complex topic. Internally displaced people (IDPs) are just one type.

Like refugees, IDPs have been forced to leave their homes in order to flee from conflict or persecution. However, the fundamental difference between the two groups is that, while refugees leave their country of origin and cross at least one border to find safety, IDPs move to another part of the country they already live in.

4 Choose from the reasons provided below to help you write an explanation of what might stop internally displaced people from leaving the country to find a safer place.

Physically unable to travel due to injury or disability	Worried about what will happen to family if left behind	Hope situation in their country gets better
Don't want to change jobs or school	Cannot safely get to border	Want to stay close to home
Will miss the food	Lack of money	

_____

_____

_____

_____

_____

_____

_____

_____

5 Match the term to its description.

refugee	Someone who has to rely on their own government for protection from violence and persecution in their home country
asylum seeker	Someone who is protected by international law if they seek safety in another country
internally displaced person	Someone who has not yet been granted refugee status but can be granted the right to stay somewhere safe for a temporary amount of time

6 Consider some of the benefits of having different types of protection for those fleeing dangerous situations. Complete the spider diagram with your ideas. Then briefly explain whether you think it's better to have more than one type of protection.

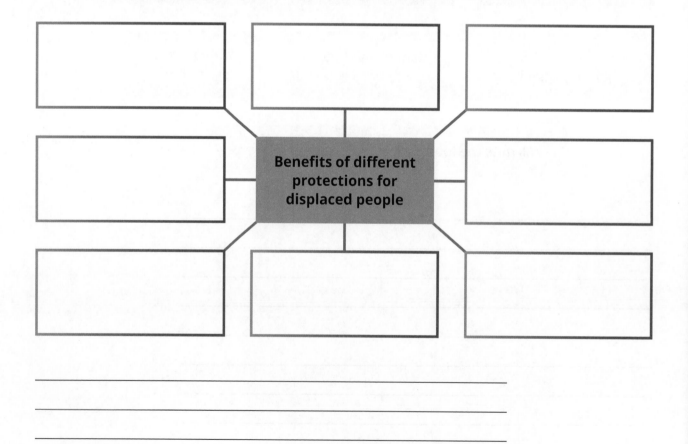

Benefits of different protections for displaced people

_____

_____

_____

_____

7 Now consider some of the benefits for the countries accepting to host displaced people. Complete the spider diagram with your ideas.

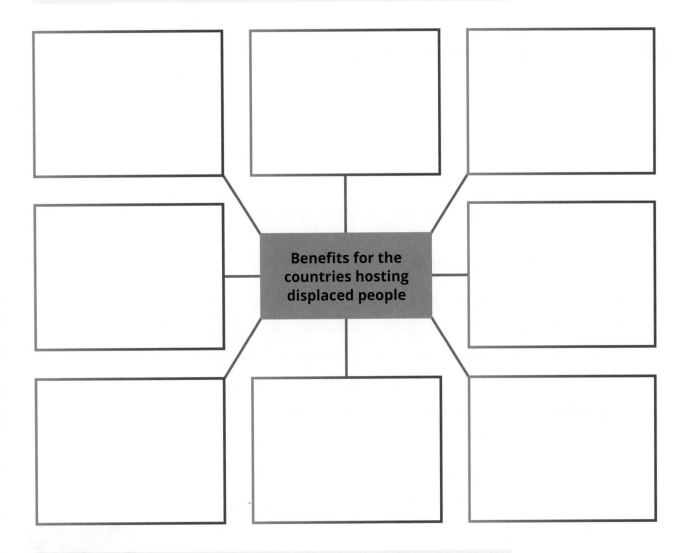

Benefits for the countries hosting displaced people

8 Explain whether refugees should have to return to their country once it is safe, or be allowed to stay where they are. (If they want to stay, they will need to request residency and official citizenship in their new country.)

_____

_____

_____

_____

_____

_____

Life as a refugee, asylum seeker or internally displaced person can be difficult to imagine. However, for 79.5 million people around the world, it is an unfortunate reality.

9   Read the text above and then answer the questions.

1   What can be done to support these people?

_____

_____

_____

_____

2   Who can help to provide this support?

_____

_____

_____

_____

3   What **rights** would they immediately need to address?

_____

_____

_____

_____

4   Do you think this would be easy to do?

_____

_____

_____

_____

5   What might stop a country's government from providing this help?

_____

_____

_____

_____

The **United Nations High Commissioner for Refugees** does a lot to help safeguard and support refugees, asylum seekers and internally displaced people. However, there are many practical ways in which you yourself can help refugees.

10 Match the practical ways to help refugees with examples of these.

Host them in your home	Spread the word to your friends, family, and classmates about ways they can help as well.
Volunteer a special skill	Organise ways in your school or community to raise money to help refugees.
Help them integrate into the culture and community	Teach them your country's language. The ability to communicate with others is important for people to be able to ask for, and receive, their basic needs.
Raise awareness	Introduce them to groups that you are a part of.
Organise fundraising events	Check with your local charity what items they may need, for example books or old mobile phones or computers.
Donate	Discuss with your parents/guardians if it would be possible to offer a vacant room in your home to a refugee.

According to the **United Nations**, the right to adequate food is realised when every man, woman and child, alone or in a community with others, has physical and economic access to adequate food or the means for obtaining it. Unfortunately, displaced people do not always have access to adequate food.

11   Read the definitions of the four key elements of the right to food, and label them with the terms below.

Accessibility   Adequacy   Availability   Sustainability

_____ : food should be obtainable from natural resources, either through the production of food, by cultivating land and animal farming, or through other ways like fishing, hunting or gathering. Food should also be on sale in markets and shops.

_____ : food should be accessible for both present and future generations.

_____ : food must satisfy dietary needs, taking into account, for example, a person's age, living conditions, health, occupation and gender. Food should be safe for human consumption and free from adverse substances.

_____ : food must be affordable and individuals should be able to have an adequate diet without compromising on other basic needs, such as education, medicines and rent. Food should be accessible to all, including the physically vulnerable, such as children, sick people, people with disabilities and the elderly. Food must also be available to people in remote areas, to victims of armed conflicts or natural disasters, and to prisoners.

12 Say whether you think it's possible to have some of the four elements listed in Activity 11 without the others. Explain your answer.

_____

_____

_____

_____

_____

_____

_____

13 In fewer than 20 words, explain the work of the United Nations High Commissioner for Refugees.

_____

_____

_____

_____

_____

What new things have you learned?

What had you not thought about before?

Human rights defenders

HR8.5D – Knowledge about NGOs, charities and organisations that work towards the prevention of trafficking and other types of modern slavery.

We will learn:

- what modern slavery and human trafficking are
- what a non-government organisation (NGO) is and what it does
- how charities can support human rights.

Key vocabulary

charities, humans, non-government organisation (NGO), rights, United Nations, violations

Even though slavery has been abolished, and organisations like the **United Nations** have been established to ensure and protect people's rights, you may be surprised that slavery still exists in the modern world. What's even more shocking is that modern slavery, in its many forms, happens in every country in the world, with millions of children and adults trapped by it.

It is important to understand the rights that all **humans** are entitled to so you can spot when they are being violated and know what can be done about this.

Modern slavery is the severe exploitation of other people for personal or commercial gain, and can occur in plain sight. People can become entrapped making our clothes, serving our food, picking our crops, working in factories, or working in houses as cooks, cleaners or childcare providers.

Many have fallen into this oppressive trap simply because they were trying to escape poverty or insecurity, improve their lives and support their families.

1 Tick all the indicators that you can look for to spot the signs of modern slavery.

☐ Appears to be under the control of someone else

☐ Regularly goes out with people in social settings

☐ Reluctant to interact with others or the authorities

☐ Has no personal identification on them

☐ Usually accepts invitations to visit other's homes

☐ Has few personal belongings; wears the same clothes every day or wears unsuitable clothes for work

☐ Not able to move around freely

☐ Appears frightened, withdrawn, or shows signs of physical or psychological abuse

☐ Upbeat and positive about their job but also talks openly about what they get up to in their free time

☐ Always dropped off and collected for work in the same way by the same person, especially at unusual times (for example, very early in the morning or late at night)

2 Choose **four** key words that can be used to easily remember these indicators.

_____   _____

_____   _____

From the outside, modern slavery can look like a normal job. However, people are being controlled – they can face violence or abuse, be forced into inescapable debt, or have had their passport taken away and be threatened with deportation.

3   Create a poster that **either** offers advice that **non-government organisations (NGOs)**, **charities** and other organisations can share with people to avoid them being lured into slavery **or** that encourages people to join an anti-slavery movement. You may want to include a memorable slogan and/or logo to make your message more memorable.

4 Answer the questions below to show your understanding of modern-day slavery.

1 What can you do to let someone who might be enslaved know they can trust you?

_____

_____

_____

_____

2 What kinds of things can you do to help someone who has told you they are a victim of modern slavery?

_____

_____

_____

_____

_____

_____

3 How can people around the world work together to put an end to modern slavery?

_____

_____

_____

_____

_____

_____

4 What organisations do you know that take action against **rights violations** like modern slavery?

- _____

- _____

- _____

What new things have you learned?

What had you not thought about before?

Good governance

We will learn:

- about historical examples of discrimination
- how **mistreatment** by those in power can result in discrimination
- what laws have been put in place to stop misuse of power.

Key vocabulary

discrimination, dominance, governance, government, laws, mistreatment, misuse, power

According to various social science and political definitions, power is generally defined as the capacity to influence the actions, beliefs or behaviour of others. Simply put, power is having the ability to cause or prevent an action – the discretion to act or not act. Those in power, especially when elected, have a duty not to intentionally abuse or misuse it.

Imagine you have just become one of the most powerful world leaders. What decisions would you make? Would your decisions benefit your nation's people or the economy? Do you think it's possible to benefit both? Can you be certain that the decisions you make will be the right ones? What would you do to ensure people respect and think of you as a good leader?

Over time, the word '**power**' has had many definitions and has been used in a variety of contexts.

1 Read the definitions of 'power' and then give your own examples or scenarios of where that type of power might be used.

Definition 1: possession of control, authority or influence over others

_____

_____

Definition 2: possession of the qualities (especially mental) required to do or get something done

_____

_____

Definition 3: possession of physical might

_____

_____

Definition 4: possession of a source or means of supplying energy

_____

_____

2 Suggest **one** thing these definitions have in common. Explain what you think this says about our beliefs about power.

_____

_____

_____

_____

_____

3 Use the spider diagram to list some of the ways you have power, according to the definitions from Activity 1.

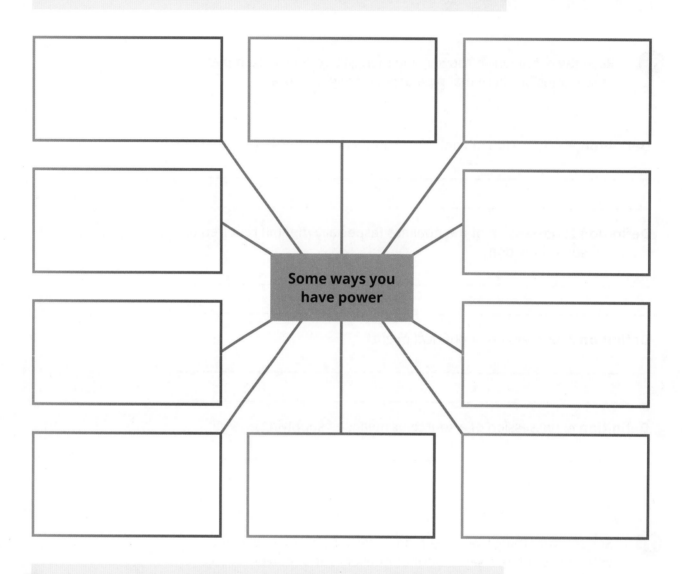

Some ways you have power

4 Pick the **three** powers from your spider diagram that you most value. Explain why you chose them.

1 _____

_____

_____

2 _____

_____

_____

3 _____

_____

_____

5   Fill in the spider diagram to list some of the ways that others
have power over you, according to the definitions from Activity 1.

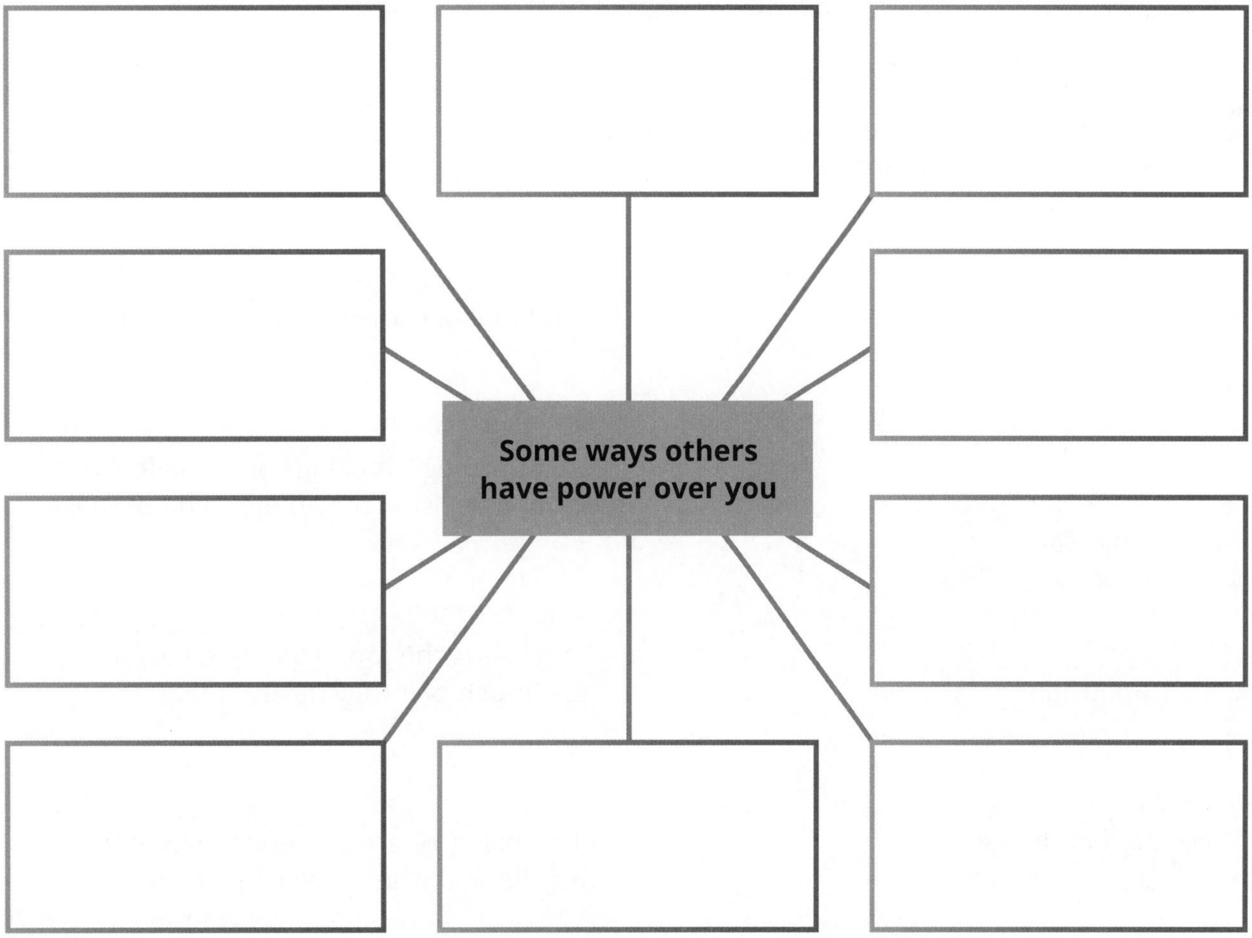

Some ways others have power over you

6   Look again at your spider diagram above and then answer
the questions.

1   Who are the people that enforce powers?

- _____
- _____
- _____

- _____
- _____
- _____

2   Which powers are for your safety and how do they keep you safe?

_____

_____

_____

_____

_____

According to Definition 1 (see Activity 1), power can be defined as the 'possession of control, authority or influence over others'. However, there are many different ways that one person can have power over another.

7 Match the types of power with the examples provided. You will need to match more than one example to some types.

Withholding someone's money from them

Guilt tripping – making someone feel bad about a decision they did or did not make

physical

financial

Controlling the food someone eats and how much of it they have

mental/emotional

Controlling where someone goes, what they do and when they come back

Enforcing a system that limits someone's spending; creating a budget

8 Pick **one** type of power from the list above and write another example for it. Try to make your example seem like a good use of the power.

_____

_____

_____

_____

'Power' is often defined in negative terms and as a form of **dominance**. However, it can also be a positive force – both for individuals and for communities/groups – to act for change.

9 Read the four descriptions of different expressions of power, here and on the next page. Label each to show which type of expression of power, from those listed below, is being described.

power over	power to	power with	power within

This expression of power involves finding common ground among different interests and building collective strength. It is founded on mutual support, solidarity and collaboration. These are ideals that aim to multiply individual talents and knowledge, as well as transform or reduce social conflict.

This expresses _____ .

This is the most commonly recognised expression of power. It has many negative connotations – for example, oppression, force, coercion, **discrimination**, corruption and abuse. Having this power involves taking it from someone else, and then using it to dominate and prohibit others from gaining it. It is often used in politics.

This expresses _____ .

Depending on a person's sense of self-worth and self-knowledge, this expression of power includes the ability to recognise individual qualities, while respecting others. Possessing this power means having the capacity to imagine and have hope. It affirms the common human quest for dignity and fulfilment. The extent of this power and its success is not dictated by external agencies.

This expresses _____ .

This expression of power suggests that every individual possesses the unique potential to shape their life and world. Personal development plays an integral role in this expression as it is based on the belief that the individual has the ability to make a difference, to create something new or to achieve goals.

This expresses _____ .

10 Circle **two** of the four expressions of power typically used by an entrepreneur starting a new business.

| power over | power with | power within | power to |

11 Circle **one** of the four expressions of power typically used by a volunteer who works in support of a climate change initiative.

| power over | power with | power within | power to |

12 Circle **one** of the four expressions of power typically used by most governments and world-leading groups. Then list some strategies that a **government** may use to exert this expression of power.

| power over | power with | power within | power to |

- _____
- _____
- _____
- _____
- _____

Good governance is a process whereby public establishments conduct public affairs and manage public resources in a manner that promotes the rule of law and the recognition of human rights.

13 Read the definition of good governance above and then answer the questions.

1 By this definition, who is good governance designed to serve?

_____

2 What **two** areas are governing institutions responsible for?

1 _____

2 _____

14 Put these examples into the two areas of responsibility you identified in Activity 13.

| Effective healthcare for all | Guaranteeing human well-being | Sustainable development |

| The right to sufficient food | Quality education for young people | Adequate housing for all |

| A fair justice system for all | Personal security for all citizens |

Area 1: _____	**Area 2:** _____

Studies have shown that good **governance** improves life evaluations. The improvements can be direct, because people are happier living in a context of good government. They can also be indirect, because good governance enables people to achieve higher levels of something else directly important to their well-being.

15 Rank these outcomes of good governance. The most important outcomes for public well-being should be at the top and the least important at the bottom.

| facilities for personal development | sufficient provisions for the unemployed | adequate childcare facilities |

| sustainable development | sufficient food | quality education | adequate security |

| fair justice system | quality healthcare | adequate housing |

Bad governance is characterised by a lack of transparency and accountability, uninformed policy making, and deceiving those being governed. In an effort to discourage bad governance, there are 12 widely agreed principles of good governance.

16   Match some of the 12 principles of good governance with their definitions.

Participation, Representation and Fair Conduct of Elections	Charges for public services do not exceed the cost of services provided and do not reduce demand excessively
Efficiency and Effectiveness	Best possible use is made of the resources available and results meet the agreed objectives
Ethical Conduct	The opportunity for active involvement by all sectors of society in the decision-making process, regarding all issues of interest
Rule of Law	Taking responsibility for actions, especially when they affect the public interest
Openness and Transparency	Human rights are respected and protected, and diversity is treated as an asset
Accountability	Consideration of the needs of future generations is reflected in current policies
Sound Financial Management	The process of decision making by those in power can be scrutinised by concerned members of society
Human Rights, Cultural Diversity and Social Cohesion	There are effective measures to prevent and combat all forms of corruption
Sustainability and Long-term Orientation	Rules and regulations are implemented in accordance with procedures provided by **laws** and are enforced impartially

17   Tick all the reasons to practise good governance.

☐   To preserve and strengthen public confidence

☐   To provide the foundation for a high-functioning society

☐   To damage or remove democratic mechanisms by exploiting or taking control of weak state institutions

☐   To pursue policies designed to create social, economic, ethnic or religious conflicts

☐   To promote division in order to gain and hold on to power

☐   To ensure the organisation is well-placed to respond to a changing external environment

18   Underline the correct words to complete the definition of good governance.

Successful good governance requires a **systematic/chaotic/simple** approach that incorporates strategic **conflicts/planning/tactics**, risk **taking/avoidance/management** and performance supervision.

19   Give an example of where people have faced discrimination because of the **misuse** of power. Your example can be from the past or a more recent situation.

_____

_____

_____

_____

_____

_____

What new things have you learned?
What had you not thought about before?

Participation and inclusion

Objective

PG8.6B – Knowledge of models of participation from around the world that demonstrate the belief that everyone is of equal value and worth.

We will learn:

- about different models of participation from around the world
- how these models can be used to demonstrate the belief that everyone is of equal value and worth.

Key vocabulary

apartheid, equal, inclusion, participation, segregation, value, worth

i   Each and every individual has abilities, as well as limits to those abilities. No one should be excluded because of any such limitations or the needs they may have as a result of them. What factors are required in order for everyone in a group to equally participate, as well as feel genuinely included?

Good governance is tightly linked to the fight against corruption, which is the abuse and misuse of entrusted power for private gain.

1 Look closely at what the definition above means for those in power. Tick all the statements that apply to each question.

1 What does it mean to abuse or misuse something?

☐ The improper use or treatment of something

☐ Something done to fairly or properly gain benefit

☐ To use something in the wrong way or for the wrong purpose

2 What does it mean for something or someone to be entrusted?

☐ To have been assigned the responsibility for doing something

☐ To have something put in your care or protection

☐ To commit to another without confidence of fulfilment

Transparency International, a non-governmental organisation, explains that the cost of corruption can be categorised according to four groups: political, social, economic and environmental.

2 Match the categories with their explanations.

political	Your participation and trust in government
social	Your opportunity to accumulate wealth
economic	Your chance for a healthy environment and a sustainable future
environmental	Your freedom and rule of law

3   Tick all the examples of private gain.

☐   Being open and honest with concerned parties about any public affairs they wish to learn more about

☐   Paying a bribe to access services like healthcare and education

☐   Operating under a justice system that treats all groups according to the rule of law

☐   Using money intended for public development for personal affairs

☐   Organised criminal activity and manipulation of votes to ensure that a leader maintains control of power, status and wealth

☐   Providing adequate resources to ensure basic human rights are met

☐   Providing or receiving gifts, entertainment and hospitality or other items of **value**, such as donations, sponsorships and internships in return for guaranteed votes

Apartheid – or 'apartness' in the language of Afrikaans – is a historical example of the misuse of power. Apartheid was a system, backed by rule of law, that upheld segregationist policies against non-white citizens.

4   Read the text above and then answer the questions.

1   Which words tell you there was a separation of groups under the apartheid system?

_____

_____

2   Which group were the segregationist policies in favour of?

_____

3   Which group suffered as a result of the segregationist policies?

_____

Read the text below, which gives a brief overview of apartheid. Then answer the questions on this and the next page.

After the National Party gained power in South Africa in 1948, its all-white government immediately began enforcing existing policies of racial **segregation**. Under apartheid, Non-White South Africans (a majority of the population) would be forced to live in separate areas from whites and to use separate public facilities. Contact between the two groups would be limited.

Despite strong and consistent opposition to apartheid within and outside of South Africa, its laws remained in effect for the better part of 50 years.

The effects of apartheid touched every aspect of daily life. By 1950, marriage and relations between White and Non-White South Africans were banned, while a series of Land Acts meant more than 80 per cent of the country's land was set aside for the white minority. Black men and women were forced to live in ten so-called 'Black homelands' known as Bantustans, where they were permitted to run businesses. To live and work in designated 'white areas', they required permits. Hospitals, ambulances, buses and public facilities were all segregated, and non-white participation in government was denied.

1 Complete the table below to show what the whites and non-whites who lived in South Africa were able to do during apartheid. You will need to use some inference to compare and contrast the information.

Whites in South Africa	Non-whites in South Africa

2   The majority of South Africa's population were not white. Yet 'more
    than 80 per cent of the country's land was set aside for the white
    minority'. During apartheid, the Black homelands were called
    Bantustans. What can you infer about the quality of life among the
    two groups? Use the map to help you.

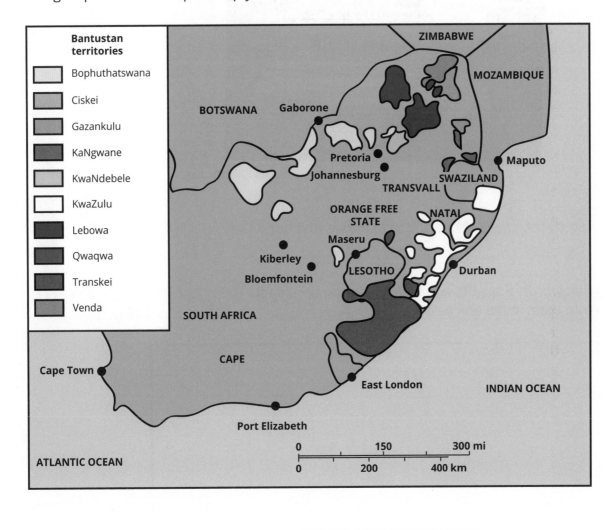

_____

_____

_____

_____

_____

6   Look again at the map and describe what is suggested by the
    positioning of the Bantustans (Black homelands)?

_____

_____

_____

7   Study the image above and then answer the questions.

1   What words, thoughts and feelings do you have about this image? Write them in the box below.

2   How do images like this explain the historical misuse of power and the promotion of exclusion rather than **inclusion**?

Nelson Mandela, one of the leaders of the African National Congress (ANC), used the words below to demonstrate the belief that everyone is of **equal** value and **worth**.

> A nation should not be judged by how it treats its highest citizens, but its lowest ones.

8 Explain how you think Mandela's words encouraged **participation** and inclusion by expressing the belief that everyone needed to work together to end the bad governance in South Africa at the time.

_____

_____

_____

_____

_____

_____

_____

9 Many models of participation from around the world suggest that citizen participation equals citizen power. Select the examples that support this theory.

☐ Consultation among all groups

☐ Making decisions that will impact all without conference or agreement

☐ Sharing information

☐ Helping the group of belonging before any others

☐ Collaborative decision making

☐ Acting together in support of initiatives

Over the years, resistance to apartheid within South Africa took many forms. It included non-violent demonstrations, protests and strikes, to political action and, eventually, to armed resistance. Together with the South Indian National Congress, the African National Congress (ANC) organised a mass meeting in 1952, during which attendees burned their passbooks. In 1955, a group called the Congress of the People adopted a Freedom Charter asserting that 'South Africa belongs to all who live in it, Black or white'.

By 1961, most resistance leaders had been captured and either sentenced to long prison terms or executed. Nelson Mandela, a founder of uMkhonto we Sizwe ('Spear of the Nation') – the military wing of the ANC – was imprisoned from 1962 to 1990. His imprisonment would draw international attention and help gain support for the anti-apartheid cause. On 10 June 1980, his followers smuggled out a letter from Mandela in prison and made it public.

In 1976, when thousands of Black children in Soweto – a Bantustan in Johannesburg – demonstrated against the Afrikaans language requirement for Black African students, the police opened fire with tear gas and bullets. This brought further international attention and, in 1985, the United Kingdom and the United States of America imposed economic sanctions on the country.

On 11 February 1990, Mandela was freed. This was followed by a new constitution, which enfranchised Blacks and other racial groups, taking effect in 1994. Elections that year led to a coalition (shared-party) government with a non-white majority, marking the official end of the apartheid system.

10 Look back at the text on the previous page. Create a timeline of events leading up to the end of apartheid.

What new things have you learned?

What had you not thought about before?

advertising – the activity or business of advertising things on television, in newspapers, and such like

Agent of Change – a person who inspires others to make or support change

Amnesty International – an organisation that supports rights, especially people's right to express their beliefs without being punished

anthropocentric – the belief that human beings are more important than anything else in existence

apartheid – the former political and social system in South Africa, in which only white people had full political rights and people of other ethnicities, especially Black people, were forced to go to separate schools, live in separate areas, and so on

asteroids – the many small bodies (of rock, for example) that move around the Sun, especially between Mars and Jupiter

asylum seekers – people who leave their own country because they are in danger, especially for political reasons, and who ask the government of another country to allow them to live there

autism – a developmental disability that can affect how people communicate or form relationships

awareness – knowledge or understanding of a particular subject, situation or thing

benefit (noun) – advantage, improvement or help that you get from something

benefit (verb) – to give advantage, improvement or help to someone or something

butterfly effect – the idea that a small event can have significant unintended consequences somewhere else in the world

capital resource – a building, machine, tool or other product used to produce goods or services

cause – a person, event or thing that makes something happen

cause and effect – when one thing causes something else to happen

challenge – to refuse to accept that something is right, fair or legal

change (verb) – to make something become different

change (noun) – the process or result of something or someone becoming different

charities – organisations that give money, goods or help to people who are poor, sick, and such like

climate change – a permanent change in planet Earth's weather conditions

comets – objects in space, like bright balls with long tails, that move around the Sun

commitment – a promise to do something or to behave in a particular way

commodity – a product that is bought and sold

communal – shared by a group of people or animals, especially a group who live together

community – the people who live in the same area or town and/or a group of people who share something like culture, religion or interests

compromise – to reach an agreement in which everyone involved accepts less than what they wanted at first

conflict – a state of disagreement or argument between people, groups or countries

consequences – things that happen as a result of particular actions or sets of conditions

conserve – to protect something and prevent it from changing or being damaged

constellations – groups of stars that form particular patterns and have names

contested – not agreed with or accepted by everyone

debris – the pieces of something that are left after it has been destroyed, such as in an accident or explosion

deforestation – the cutting or burning down of all the trees in an area

derelict – in very bad condition because it has not been used for a long time

development – the growth or improvement

of something, so that it becomes bigger or more advanced

discrimination – the practice of treating one person or group differently from another in an unfair way

disposal – when you get rid of something

disputes – serious arguments or disagreements

dominance – the fact of being more powerful, more important or more noticeable than other people or things

egocentric – thinking only about yourself and not about what other people might need or want

emotion – a strong human feeling such as love, hate or anger

empathy – the ability to understand other people's feelings and problems

energy – power that is used to provide heat or operate machines

environment – the natural features of a place, for example, its weather, the type of land it has or the type of plants that grow in it

equal – having the same rights, opportunities and so on as everyone else, whatever your ethnicity, religion or gender

equality – a situation in which people have the same rights or advantages

equity – the principle that people may need differing

treatment to give them the same chances as others

export – to sell goods to another country

expression – something you say, write or do that shows what you think or feel

fair – treating everyone in a way that is right

fair trade – the activity of making, buying and selling goods in a way that is morally right; for example, by making sure that international labour laws are obeyed, that the environment has not been damaged by making the goods, and that the people who grow or make a product have been paid a fair price for it

fairness – the quality of being fair

family – a group of people who are related to each other, especially a mother, a father and their children

formats – the ways in which information is stored on a computer

freedom – the state of being free and the right to do what you want

future (noun) – the time after the present

future (adjective) – likely to happen or exist at a time after the present

Gaia theory – the theory that living and non-living things interact with, and depend on, each other to maintain the conditions needed for life to exist on planet Earth

galaxy – a large group of stars

gender – being either male or female of a species

global – affecting or including the whole world

global economy – the economy of the world seen as a whole

globalisation – the tendency for the world economy to work as one unit, led by large international companies doing business all over the world

globally – relating to the whole world

governance – the act or process of governing

government – the group of people who govern a country or state

hazardous – dangerous, especially to people's health or safety

healthcare – the services that are provided for looking after people's health, or the activity of doing this

heritage – the traditional beliefs, values, customs and such like of a family, country or society

human – belonging to or relating to people, especially as opposed to machines or animals

human resource – a skill provided by a person

identity – who or what something or someone is

immigration – entering another country to live there permanently

impact – the effect or influence that something such as an event or situation has on someone or something

import – to bring a product from one country into another so that it can be sold there

inclusion – the act of involving someone or something in a larger group or set, or the fact of being involved in one

industry – businesses that produce a particular type of thing or provide a particular service

inequality – an unfair situation, in which some groups in society have more money, opportunities and power than others

influence (noun) – someone or something that has the power to affect the way someone develops, behaves or thinks, without using direct force or orders

influence (verb) – to affect the way someone develops, behaves or thinks, without directly forcing or ordering them

initiatives – new plans or processes to achieve a particular aim or to solve a particular problem

injustice – a situation in which people are treated very unfairly and not given their rights

innovations – new ideas, methods or inventions

instrumental value – the worth of someone or something based on its ability to help achieve a goal

interdependence – a situation or relationship in which people or things depend on each other

internally displaced – forced to leave a local area or region (especially during a conflict, or for political or religious reasons) but staying within the borders of the home country

intrinsic value – the worth of someone or something regardless of its ability to help achieve a goal

judgement – an opinion formed about someone or something

justice – fairness in the way people are treated

laws – rules that people in a particular country or area must obey

manufacturing – the process of making things with the use of machines

marginalised – made to feel unimportant and powerless in an unfair way

media – all the organisations, such as television, radio and newspapers, that provide news and information for the public

medicine development – the process of researching new drugs or medicines and bringing them to market

meteoroids – small objects (for example, lumps of rock) that orbit the Sun

migration – moving to a new country for the purposes of work or for an alternative, better lifestyle

misinformation – incorrect information, especially when deliberately intended to deceive people

mistreatment – the unfair or cruel treatment of people by those in a position of authority

misuse (noun) – the dishonest or wrong use of something

misuse (verb) – to use something for the wrong purpose or in the wrong way, often with harmful results

natural resource – something that exists in nature and can be used by people, for example, oil, trees

negative – harmful, unpleasant or not wanted

non-government organisation (NGO) – an organisation, often non-profit-making, that works independently of the government

non-judgemental – an opinion on something which is not biased by moral or personal feelings

open-minded – being willing to listen to other people's ideas and views

opportunity – a chance to do something or an occasion when it is easy for you to do something

organisations – companies, businesses or groups that have been formed for a particular purpose

outsourcing – when a company uses workers from outside the company to do a job

participation – the act of taking part in an activity or event

patents – special documents that give you the right to make or sell new inventions or products that no one else is allowed to copy

perspective – a way of thinking about something, especially one which is influenced by the type of person you are or by your experiences

pharmaceutical – relating to the production of drugs and medicines

planet – a body in space that orbits around the Sun

political – relating to the government, politics and public affairs of a country

politics – ideas and activities relating to gaining and using power in a country, city, state and such like

pollution – the process of making air, water and soil dangerously dirty and not suitable for people to use, or the state of being dangerously dirty

positionality – the concept that how we understand the world is influenced by our personal values, our opinions and where we live

positive – if you are positive about things, you are hopeful and confident, and think about what is good in a situation rather than what is bad; expressing support, agreement or approval

poverty – the situation or experience of being poor

power – the ability or right to control people or events

prejudice – an unreasonable dislike and distrust of people who are different from you in some way, especially because of their ethnicity, gender or religion

principles – moral rules or beliefs about what is right and wrong that influence how you behave

privilege – a special advantage that is given only to one person or group of people

projection – a representation of something solid on a flat surface, such as a map

recycle – to treat used objects or materials so that they can be used again

refugees – people who have been forced to leave their country, especially during a conflict, or for political or religious reasons

reliable – someone or something that can be trusted or depended on

repurpose – to change something for it to be used in a new, different way

resolution – the solving of a problem, argument or difficult situation

reuse – use something again (land, for example), perhaps for a different purpose

rights – something that you are allowed to do or have

scientific data – information or facts used for a scientific purpose

segregation – when people of different ethnicities, gender or religions are kept apart so that they live, work or study separately

self-regulating – not reliant on outside factors or influences for control

society – a particular large group of people who share laws, organisations and customs

solution – a way of sorting out a problem or dealing with a difficult situation

sources – things, places, activities and so on from which you get something

space junk – artificial objects in space that are broken or destroyed and can no longer serve their original purpose

space race – the competition between the United States of America and the Soviet Union to achieve superiority in space following the Second World War

species – a group of animals or plants whose members are similar and can breed together to produce young animals or plants

stars – huge balls of burning gas in space that can be seen at night as a point of light in the sky

stereotype – an often unfair or untrue belief or idea of what a particular type of person or thing is like

structural – connected with or relating to the structure of something

structures – in society, these are the groups that people are said to belong to and can define people's perceptions of their values and worth. Structures could, for example, be based around family, religion, gender, law or money

supply chain – the series of organisations that are involved in passing products from manufacturers to the public

sustainability – the ability to continue without causing damage to the environment

sustainable – able to continue without causing damage to the environment

systemic – relating to

or affecting the whole of a system

systems – groups of related parts that work together as a whole for a particular purpose

toxic – containing poison or caused by poisonous substances

trade agreement – an agreement between countries to help each other trade, for example, by buying and selling to each other at lower prices than usual

trials – testing to find out whether a new drug or medicine works effectively and is safe

unfair – not treating everyone in a way that is right

United Nations – an international organisation that tries to find peaceful solutions to world problems

United Nations Development Programme (UNDP) – the United Nations agency responsible for monitoring and working

to eliminate poverty and inequality around the world

United Nations High Commissioner for Refugees (UNHCR) – the United Nations agency responsible for helping refugees and internally displaced and stateless people

unsanctioned – not allowed; forbidden in law

value – the importance or usefulness of something or someone

violation – an action that breaks a law, agreement or principle

waste – unwanted materials or substances that are left after you have used something

wealthy – having a lot of money or possessions

well-being – a feeling of being comfortable, healthy and happy

worth – the importance or usefulness of something or someone